weightwatchers360° cookbook

Turn up the flavor

200 delicious recipes that pack a punch

D1249390

about weight watchers

WEIGHT WATCHERS INTERNATIONAL, INC. is the world's leading provider of weight-management services, operating globally through a network of company-owned and franchise operations. Weight Watchers holds nearly 45,000 meetings each week worldwide, at which members receive group support and education about healthful eating patterns, behavior modification, and physical activity. Weight-loss and weight-management results vary by individual. We recommend that you attend Weight Watchers meetings to benefit from the supportive environment and follow the comprehensive Weight Watchers program, which includes a food plan, an activity plan, and a behavioral component. **WeightWatchers.com** provides subscription weight-management products, such as eTools and Weight Watchers Mobile, and is the leading internet-based weight-management provider in the world. In addition, Weight Watchers offers a wide range of products, publications (including **Weight Watchers Magazine,** which is available on newsstands and in Weight Watchers meeting rooms), and programs for people interested in weight loss and control. For the Weight Watchers meeting nearest you, call **1-800-651-6000.** For information about bringing Weight Watchers to your workplace, call **1-800-8AT-WORK.**

weight watchers publishing group

VP, EDITORIAL DIRECTOR NANCY GAGLIARDI

CREATIVE DIRECTOR ED MELNITSKY

PHOTO DIRECTOR DEBORAH HARDT

MANAGING EDITOR DIANE PAVIA

ASSISTANT EDITOR KATERINA GKIONIS

FOOD EDITOR EILEEN RUNYAN

EDITOR DEBORAH MINTCHEFF

RECIPE DEVELOPERS LORI LONGBOTHAM, MAUREEN LUCHEJKO, MIRIAM RUBIN

PRODUCTION MANAGER ALAN BIEDERMAN

PHOTOGRAPHER ROMULO YANES

FOOD STYLIST ANNE DISRUDE

PROP STYLIST CARLA GONZALEZ-HART

ART DIRECTOR ELIZABETH VAN ITALLIE

DESIGNER PAULINE NEUWIRTH

on the back cover:
open-face poached egg, asparagus, and prosciutto sandwiches, page 86; **grilled cheese-crusted lamb chops with herbed potatoes**, page 127; and **so light lemon cheesecake with blueberry sauce**, page 249

about our recipes

WHILE LOSING WEIGHT ISN'T only about what you eat, Weight Watchers realizes the critical role it plays in your success and overall good health. That's why our philosophy is to offer great-tasting, easy recipes that are nutritious as well as delicious. We make every attempt to use wholesome ingredients and to ensure that our recipes fall within the recommendations of the U.S. Dietary Guidelines for Americans for a diet that promotes health and reduces the risk for disease. If you have special dietary needs, consult with your health-care professional for advice on a diet that is best for you, then adapt these recipes to meet your specific nutritional needs.

To achieve these good-health goals and get the maximum satisfaction from the foods you eat, we suggest you keep the following information in mind while preparing our recipes:

weight watchers 360° and good nutrition

▶ Recipes in this book have been developed for Weight Watchers members who are following Weight Watchers 360°. **PointsPlus®** values are given for each recipe. They're assigned based on the amount of protein (grams), carbohydrates (grams), fat (grams), and fiber (grams) contained in a single serving of a recipe.

▶ Recipes include approximate nutritional information: they are analyzed for Calories (Cal), Total Fat, Saturated Fat (Sat Fat), Trans Fat, Cholesterol (Chol), Sodium (Sod), Carbohydrates (Carb), Sugar, Dietary Fiber (Fib), Protein (Prot), and Calcium (Calc). The nutritional values are calculated by registered dietitians, using nutrition analysis software.

▶ Substitutions made to the ingredients will alter the per-serving nutritional information and may affect the **PointsPlus** value.

▶ Our recipes meet Weight Watchers Good Health Guidelines for eating lean proteins and fiber-rich whole grains and for having at least five servings of vegetables and fruits and two servings of low-fat or fat-free dairy products a day, while limiting your intake of saturated fat, sugar, and sodium.

▶ Health agencies recommend limiting sodium intake. To stay in line with this recommendation, we keep sodium levels in our recipes reasonably low; to boost flavor, we often include fresh herbs or a squeeze of citrus instead of salt. If you don't have to restrict your sodium, feel free to add a touch more salt as desired.

▶ In the recipes, a green triangle (▲) indicates Weight Watchers® Power Foods.

▶ Stay on Track suggestions have a **PointsPlus** value of 0 unless otherwise stated.

▶ Recipes that work with the Simply Filling technique are listed on page 281. Find more details about this technique at your meeting.

▶ For information about the science behind lasting weight loss and more, please visit **WeightWatchers. com/science**.

PointsPlus value not what you expected?

▶ You might expect some of the **PointsPlus** values in this book to be lower when some of the foods they're made from, such as fruits and vegetables, have no **PointsPlus** values. Fruit and veggies have no **PointsPlus** values when served as a snack or part of a meal, like a cup of berries with a sandwich. But if these foods are part of a recipe, their fiber and nutrient content are incorporated into the recipe calculations. These nutrients can affect the **PointsPlus** value.

▶ Alcohol is included in our **PointsPlus** calculations. Because alcohol information is generally not included on nutrition labels, it's not an option to include when using the hand calculator or the online calculator. But since we include alcohol information that we get from our nutritionists, you might notice discrepancies between the **PointsPlus** values you see in our recipes, and the values you get using the calculator. The **PointsPlus** values listed for our recipes are the most accurate values.

shopping for ingredients

As you learn to eat healthier and add more Power Foods to your meals, remember these tips for choosing foods wisely:

LEAN MEATS AND POULTRY Purchase lean meats and poultry, and trim them of all visible fat before cooking. When poultry is cooked with the skin on, we recommend removing the skin before eating. Nutritional information for recipes that include meat, poultry, and fish is based on cooked, skinless boneless portions (unless otherwise stated), with the fat trimmed.

SEAFOOD Whenever possible, our recipes call for seafood that is sustainable and deemed the most healthful for human consumption so that your choice of seafood is not only good for the oceans but also good for you. For more information about the best seafood choices and to download a pocket guide, go to **environmentaldefensefund.org** or **montereybayaquarium.org**. For information about mercury and seafood go to **weightwatchers.com**.

PRODUCE For best flavor, maximum nutrient content, and the lowest prices, buy fresh local produce, such as vegetables, leafy greens, and fruits, in season. Rinse them thoroughly before using, and keep a supply of cut-up vegetables and fruits in your refrigerator for convenient healthy snacks.

WHOLE GRAINS Explore your market for whole-grain products such as whole wheat and whole-grain breads and pastas, brown rice, bulgur, barley, cornmeal, whole wheat couscous, oats, and quinoa to enjoy with your meals.

preparation and measuring

READ THE RECIPE Take a couple of minutes to read through the ingredients and directions before you start to prepare a recipe. This will prevent you from discovering midway through that you don't have an important ingredient or that a recipe requires several hours of marinating. And it's also a good idea to assemble all ingredients and utensils within easy reach before you begin a recipe.

WEIGHING AND MEASURING The success of any recipe depends on accurate weighing and measuring. The effectiveness of the Weight Watchers Program and the accuracy of the nutritional analysis depend on correct measuring as well. Use the following techniques:

▶ Weigh foods such as meat, poultry, and fish on a food scale.
▶ To measure liquids, use a standard glass or plastic measuring cup placed on a level surface. For amounts less than ¼ cup, use standard measuring spoons.
▶ To measure dry ingredients, use metal or plastic measuring cups that come in ¼-, ⅓-, ½-, and 1-cup sizes. Fill the appropriate cup, and level it with the flat edge of a knife or spatula. For amounts less than ¼ cup, use standard measuring spoons.

BLACK SKILLET JALAPEÑO
CORN BREAD, P. 104

contents

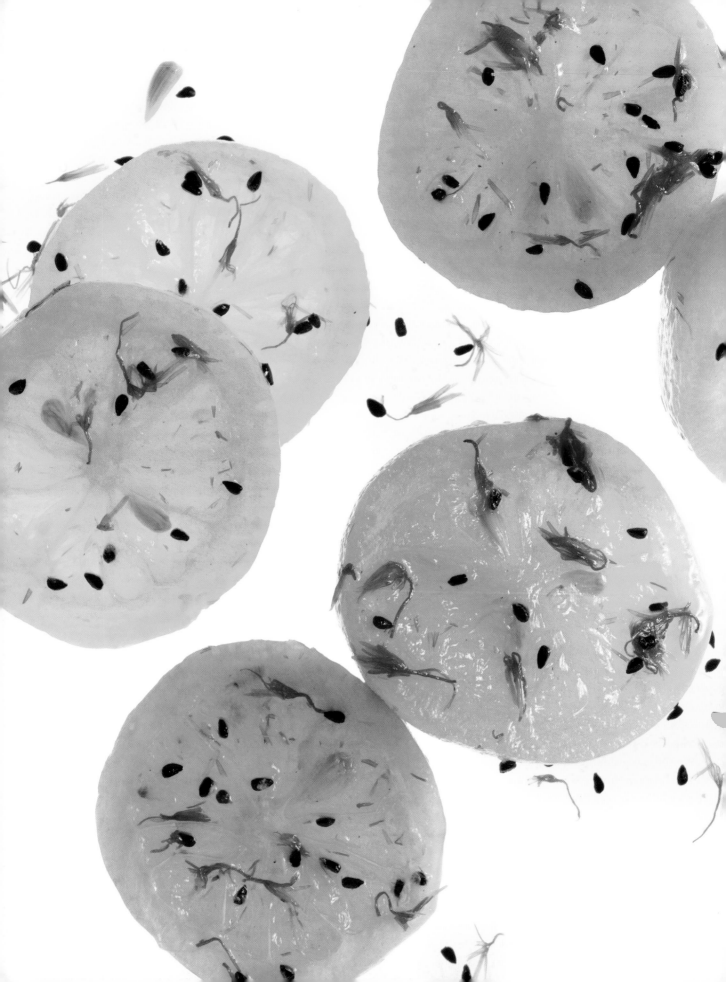

chapter 1

finger foods
light bites and snacks

artichoke-parmesan dip with black pepper pita crisps

SERVES 8

▲ **½ (14-ounce) can artichoke hearts, drained**

▲ **⅓ cup canned chickpeas, rinsed and drained**

¼ cup finely grated Parmesan cheese

1½ teaspoons olive oil

1 large garlic clove, minced

Finely grated zest and juice of ½ lemon

½ teaspoon black pepper

Several drops chipotle pepper sauce or to taste

2 tablespoons finely chopped fresh parsley

2 (6½-inch) whole wheat pita breads

1 Preheat oven to 375°F.

2 Combine artichoke hearts, chickpeas, Parmesan, oil, garlic, lemon zest and juice, ¼ teaspoon of black pepper, and the pepper sauce in food processor; pulse until smooth. Add parsley and pulse to combine. Transfer dip to serving bowl.

3 Split each pita in half to make 2 rounds. Place halves, rough side up, on work surface. Lightly spray with olive oil nonstick spray and sprinkle with remaining ¼ teaspoon black pepper. Cut each round into 8 wedges and arrange on rimmed baking sheet in single layer. Bake until lightly browned and crisp, about 8 minutes.

4 Transfer pita crisps to serving plate or basket and serve alongside dip. Dip can be refrigerated in airtight container up to 2 days. Pita crisps can be stored in airtight container at room temperature up to 2 days.

PER SERVING (1½ *tablespoons dip and 4 pita crisps*): 81 Cal, 2 g Total Fat, 1 g Sat Fat, 0 g Trans Fat, 2 mg Chol, 212 mg Sod, 13 g Carb, 1 g Sugar, 2 g Fib, 4 g Prot, 36 mg Calc.

now try this

Chipotle pepper sauce is made from red jalapeño peppers that have been slowly smoked over a smoldering fire, which imbues them with deep smoky flavor. This pepper sauce can be sprinkled over grilled chicken, pork, or fish or added to marinades, dressings, or sauces.

creamy sun-dried tomato and ricotta dip

SERVES 8 • 20 MINUTES

2
PointsPlus®
value
PER SERVING

stay
on
track

 1 (15-ounce) container fat-free ricotta cheese

 ⅓ cup sun-dried tomatoes (not packed in oil), chopped

¼ cup reduced-fat mayonnaise

 2 scallions, chopped

2 tablespoons finely grated Parmesan cheese

1 large garlic clove, minced

Pinch cayenne

¼ cup lightly packed fresh basil leaves, thinly sliced

Combine all ingredients except basil in food processor and process until smooth. Transfer to serving bowl and stir in all but 1 tablespoon of basil. Sprinkle with remaining basil.

PER SERVING (*about ⅓ cup*): 63 Cal, 1 g Total Fat, 0 g Sat Fat, 0 g Trans Fat, 5 mg Chol, 198 mg Sod, 5 g Carb, 3 g Sugar, 0 g Fib, 8 g Prot, 188 mg Calc.

Keep the *PointsPlus* value low (*and* fill yourself up) by serving this dip with a colorful array of veggie dippers. Try celery sticks, baby-cut carrots, broccoli and cauliflower florets, small white mushrooms, and Belgian endive leaves.

smoky guacamole

SERVES 8 • 20 MINUTES

2 Hass avocados, halved and pitted

1½ tablespoons lime juice

▲ 1 large plum tomato, seeded and cut into ¼-inch dice

¼ cup chopped fresh cilantro

▲ ¼ cup finely chopped red onion

1 small garlic clove, minced

½–¾ teaspoon chipotle chile powder

½ teaspoon ground cumin

½ teaspoon salt

1 With spoon, scoop avocado flesh into medium bowl. Sprinkle with lime juice and toss to prevent avocado from browning. With sharp knife, cut through avocado until chunks form, then with fork, gently mash avocado leaving it chunky.

2 Add all remaining ingredients to avocado and gently stir until combined. Serve at once or press piece of plastic wrap directly onto surface to prevent guacamole from browning. Refrigerate up to 3 hours. For best flavor, let guacamole stay out at room temperature about 1 hour before serving.

PER SERVING (*about ¼ cup*): 63 Cal, 5 g Total Fat, 1 g Sat Fat, 0 g Trans Fat, 0 mg Chol, 151 mg Sod, 4 g Carb, 1 g Sugar, 3 g Fib, 1 g Prot, 9 mg Calc.

white bean, preserved lemon, and tuna bruschetta

SERVES 8

5
PointsPlus®
value

PER SERVING

- 1 piece preserved lemon
- ▲ 1 (15½-ounce) can cannellini (white kidney) beans, rinsed and drained
- ▲ ¼ cup finely diced red onion
- 1 tablespoon lemon juice
- 2 teaspoons extra-virgin olive oil
- 1 garlic clove, minced
- ▲ 1 (½-pound) tuna steak, about 1 inch thick
- 1 (8-ounce) whole wheat baguette, cut on diagonal into 16 slices
- 1 tablespoon coarsely chopped fresh flat-leaf parsley

1 Scrape off pulp from preserved lemon and discard. Rinse peel under cold running water and finely chop enough to equal 2 tablespoons.

2 With fork, coarsely mash beans in medium bowl. Add preserved lemon, onion, lemon juice, oil, and garlic; stir until mixed well.

3 Spray grill rack with nonstick spray. Preheat grill to medium-high or prepare medium-high fire.

4 Lightly spray tuna with olive oil nonstick spray. Place on grill rack and grill 2–3 minutes per side for medium-rare, or until desired doneness. Transfer tuna to cutting board; let stand about 5 minutes.

5 Meanwhile, place slices of bread on grill rack and grill until well marked, 1–2 minutes per side. With long, thin knife, cut tuna into 16 slices. Place 1 slice of tuna on each slice of toast and top with about 1 tablespoon of bean mixture. Sprinkle with parsley and arrange on platter.

PER SERVING (2 *bruschetta*): 187 Cal, 4 g Total Fat, 1 g Sat Fat, 0 g Trans Fat, 14 mg Chol, 339 mg Sod, 24 g Carb, 2 g Sugar, 4 g Fib, 15 g Prot, 31 mg Calc.

now try this

Preserved lemon, also known as lemon pickle, is a popular condiment in Moroccan and South Indian dishes. To preserve lemons, they are quartered or halved then tightly packed into jars with salt and enough lemon juice to cover. They are then left at room temperature for several weeks or until fermented. Preserved lemons are very flavorful, so a little goes a long way. Find them in specialty food stores and online at www.kalustyans.com.

roast beef and horseradish cream mini sandwiches

SERVES 10

¼ cup prepared horseradish, drained

¼ cup reduced-fat sour cream

20 slices cocktail pumpernickel bread

▲ 5 (1-ounce) slices lean roast beef, trimmed and each cut into 4 pieces

▲ 20 thin cucumber slices

▲ 20 small watercress sprigs

▲ 10 cherry tomatoes, halved

1 Stir together horseradish and sour cream in small bowl. Spread evenly over one side of each slice of bread.

2 Place 1 piece of roast beef on horseradish cream side of each slice of bread. Top each sandwich with 1 slice of cucumber, 1 watercress sprig, and 1 tomato half.

PER SERVING (2 mini sandwiches): 70 Cal, 2 g Total Fat, 1 g Sat Fat, 0 g Trans Fat, 7 mg Chol, 218 mg Sod, 9 g Carb, 2 g Sugar, 1 g Fib, 5 g Prot, 49 mg Calc.

smoked trout, onion, and horseradish bites

SERVES 6

½ (8-ounce) package light cream cheese (Neufchâtel)

△ ½ cup fat-free sour cream

3 ounces skinless smoked trout fillet, broken into pieces

△ 2 tablespoons finely diced red onion

2 teaspoons prepared horseradish

⅛ teaspoon black pepper

Few drops hot pepper sauce

18 slices cocktail rye bread

Small dill sprigs for garnish

1 Preheat oven to 350°F.

2 Meanwhile, combine cream cheese and sour cream in food processor and pulse until smooth. Add trout, 1 tablespoon of onion, the horseradish, black pepper, and pepper sauce; pulse until blended. The spread can be refrigerated in airtight container up to 2 days, but let it come to room temperature before using for best flavor.

3 Arrange bread on rimmed baking sheet in single layer. Bake until lightly toasted but not dry, about 8 minutes. Let cool.

4 Spread about 1 tablespoon of trout mixture on each slice of toast; sprinkle evenly with remaining 1 tablespoon onion and cut each bite in half on diagonal. Garnish with dill sprigs.

PER SERVING (*6 pieces*): 164 Cal, 6 g Total Fat, 2 g Sat Fat, 0 g Trans Fat, 28 mg Chol, 366 mg Sod, 20 g Carb, 2 g Sugar, 2 g Fib, 8 g Prot, 100 mg Calc.

stay
on
track

Add a bit of bulk and crunch to these elegant little sandwiches by topping each one with a couple of slices of mini cucumber.

mushroom, garlic, and herb bruschetta

SERVES 6

PER SERVING

3 (6½-inch) multigrain pita breads, each cut into 6 wedges

1½ teaspoons olive oil

▲ 1 small onion, chopped

2 large garlic cloves, minced

▲ 6 ounces cremini mushrooms, chopped

1 tablespoon chopped fresh thyme + thyme leaves for sprinkling

⅛ teaspoon black pepper

2 ounces light cream cheese (Neufchâtel), softened

2 tablespoons finely grated pecorino-romano cheese

▲ 1½ tablespoons fat-free milk

1 Preheat oven to 425°F.

2 Arrange pita wedges on rimmed baking sheet in single layer. Bake until lightly browned and toasted, about 6 minutes. Let cool.

3 Heat oil in large nonstick skillet over medium heat. Add onion and garlic; cook, stirring, until onion is softened, about 5 minutes. Add mushrooms, chopped thyme, and pepper; cook, stirring occasionally, until mushrooms are lightly browned, about 10 minutes.

4 Remove skillet from heat; stir in cream cheese, pecorino-romano, and milk. Top each pita wedge with about 1 tablespoon of mushroom mixture and lightly sprinkle with thyme leaves.

PER SERVING (3 bruschetta): 145 Cal, 5 g Total Fat, 2 g Sat Fat, 0 g Trans Fat, 10 mg Chol, 250 mg Sod, 21 g Carb, 2 g Sugar, 3 g Fib, 6 g Prot, 61 mg Calc.

MUSTARDY BACON AND GRUYÈRE MINI TARTS

mustardy bacon and gruyère mini tarts

SERVES 6

2
PointsPlus®
value®

PER SERVING

1½ teaspoons olive oil

▲ ½ cup chopped leek (white and light green part)

2 slices Canadian bacon, finely chopped

▲ 2 tablespoons fat-free egg substitute

▲ 1 tablespoon fat-free half-and-half

1½ teaspoons country-style Dijon mustard

⅛ teaspoon salt

⅛ teaspoon black pepper

Pinch cayenne

12 frozen mini phyllo tart shells

¼ cup finely shredded Gruyère or Swiss cheese

1 Preheat oven to 350°F.

2 Heat oil in small nonstick skillet over medium heat. Add leek and cook, stirring, until softened, about 5 minutes. Transfer to small bowl. Add Canadian bacon to skillet and cook, stirring, until lightly browned, about 2 minutes. Add to leeks.

3 Whisk together egg substitute, half-and-half, mustard, salt, black pepper, and cayenne in small bowl.

4 Arrange tart shells on baking sheet. Divide leek-bacon mixture evenly among shells. Spoon about 1 teaspoon of egg mixture over leek mixture; sprinkle evenly with Gruyère. Bake until tip of small knife inserted into egg mixture comes out clean, about 15 minutes. Serve warm or at room temperature.

PER SERVING (2 tarts): 80 Cal, 4 g Total Fat, 2 g Sat Fat, 0 g Trans Fat, 8 mg Chol, 262 mg Sod, 6 g Carb, 0 g Sugar, 0 g Fib, 4 g Prot, 56 mg Calc.

now try this

Gruyère cheese, named after a town in Switzerland, is appreciated for its creamy texture, nutty flavor, and great melting quality. It is more flavorful than most other Swiss cheeses, especially when aged for five months or more. Gruyère, a cow's milk cheese, is a favorite for fondues, melted cheese sandwiches—such as Croque Monsieur and Croque Madame—and for topping French onion soup.

hummus and arugula salad dressed pitas

SERVES 8

4 (6½-inch) whole wheat pita breads

2 tablespoons orange juice

2 tablespoons lime juice

1 tablespoon honey

1 teaspoon ground cumin

¼ teaspoon black pepper

Pinch cayenne

▲ 6 ounces mesclun (about 8 lightly packed cups)

▲ 1 small cucumber, peeled, halved, seeded, and diced

▲ 2 plum tomatoes, seeded and chopped

▲ 2 scallions, thinly sliced on diagonal

▲ 4 large radishes with green tops, radishes thinly sliced and tops thickly sliced

¾ cup flavored hummus, such as roasted red pepper

1 Spray grill rack with nonstick spray. Preheat grill to medium-high or prepare medium-high fire.

2 Split each pita in half to make 2 rounds. Lightly spray pitas on both sides with nonstick spray. Place on grill rack and grill until well marked, about 2 minutes per side.

3 To make dressing, whisk together orange juice, lime juice, honey, cumin, black pepper, and cayenne in large bowl. Add mesclun, cucumber, tomatoes, scallions, radishes, and radish tops; toss until coated well.

4 Spread 1½ tablespoons hummus on rough side of each pita. Top evenly with salad.

PER SERVING (1 salad-topped pita): 147 Cal, 3 g Total Fat, 0 g Sat Fat, 0 g Trans Fat, 0 mg Chol, 289 mg Sod, 27 g Carb, 5 g Sugar, 4 g Fib, 5 g Prot, 16 mg Calc.

spinach-cheddar balls

SERVES 8

1 teaspoon olive oil

▲ 1 onion, finely chopped

2 garlic cloves, minced

▲ 1 (10-ounce) box frozen chopped spinach, thawed and squeezed dry

½ cup finely shredded sharp or extra-sharp Cheddar cheese

⅓ cup plain dried whole wheat bread crumbs

¼ cup finely grated Parmesan cheese

▲ 2 tablespoons fat-free egg substitute

⅓ cup Italian seasoned panko (Japanese bread crumbs)

1 Preheat oven to 350°F. Spray jelly-roll pan with nonstick spray.

2 Heat oil in medium nonstick skillet over medium heat. Add onion and cook until softened, about 5 minutes. Stir in garlic and cook until fragrant, about 1 minute longer. Remove skillet from heat and let cool about 10 minutes.

3 Mix together spinach, Cheddar, bread crumbs, Parmesan, egg substitute, and cooled onion-garlic mixture in medium bowl. Shape into 32 (1-inch) balls. Place panko on sheet of wax paper and roll balls in panko to coat. Place 1 inch apart in prepared pan; lightly spray with nonstick spray. Bake until heated through, about 12 minutes. Serve warm.

PER SERVING (*4 balls*): 99 Cal, 5 g Total Fat, 3 g Sat Fat, 0 g Trans Fat, 11 mg Chol, 248 mg Sod, 11 g Carb, 3 g Sugar, 3 g Fib, 6 g Prot, 152 mg Calc.

stay on track

Make these mini balls even more satisfying by serving a bowl of warm tomato sauce seasoned with dried oregano alongside. Don't forget toothpicks and napkins!

chicken and star fruit yakitori

SERVES 8

¼ cup reduced-sodium soy sauce

3 tablespoons mirin

3 tablespoons sake

2 tablespoons grated peeled fresh ginger

2 garlic cloves, minced

2 teaspoons sugar

▲ 1 pound skinless boneless chicken breasts, cut into 1½-inch chunks

▲ 2 star fruit, sliced and seeded

▲ 1 large red bell pepper, cut into 1½-inch pieces

1 Spray grill rack with nonstick spray. Preheat grill to medium-high or prepare medium-high fire. If using wooden skewers, soak in water 30 minutes.

2 Meanwhile, to make sauce, combine soy sauce, mirin, sake, ginger, garlic, and sugar in small saucepan; bring to boil. Reduce heat and simmer until sauce is reduced to ⅓ cup, about 6 minutes. Remove saucepan from heat.

3 Thread chicken, star fruit, and bell pepper onto 8 (10-inch) skewers dividing evenly. Place skewers on grill rack and grill, turning frequently and basting with sauce, until chicken is cooked through, about 8 minutes. Serve hot or warm.

PER SERVING (*1 skewer*): 103 Cal, 1 g Total Fat, 0 g Sat Fat, 0 g Trans Fat, 31 mg Chol, 296 mg Sod, 7 g Carb, 4 g Sugar, 1 g Fib, 12 g Prot, 11 mg Calc.

now try this

Star fruit grows in tropical climates (Hawaii, Florida, the Caribbean, and South and Central America) in clusters on small trees. Usually about 5 inches long, this fruit starts out green and turns deep yellow when ripe. A star fruit should feel heavy for its size and have evenly colored skin without bruises. If it isn't completely ripe when purchased, leave it out at room temperature until it turns yellow, then use or refrigerate up to several days. To prepare, trim off the ends of the star fruit, then slice or dice.

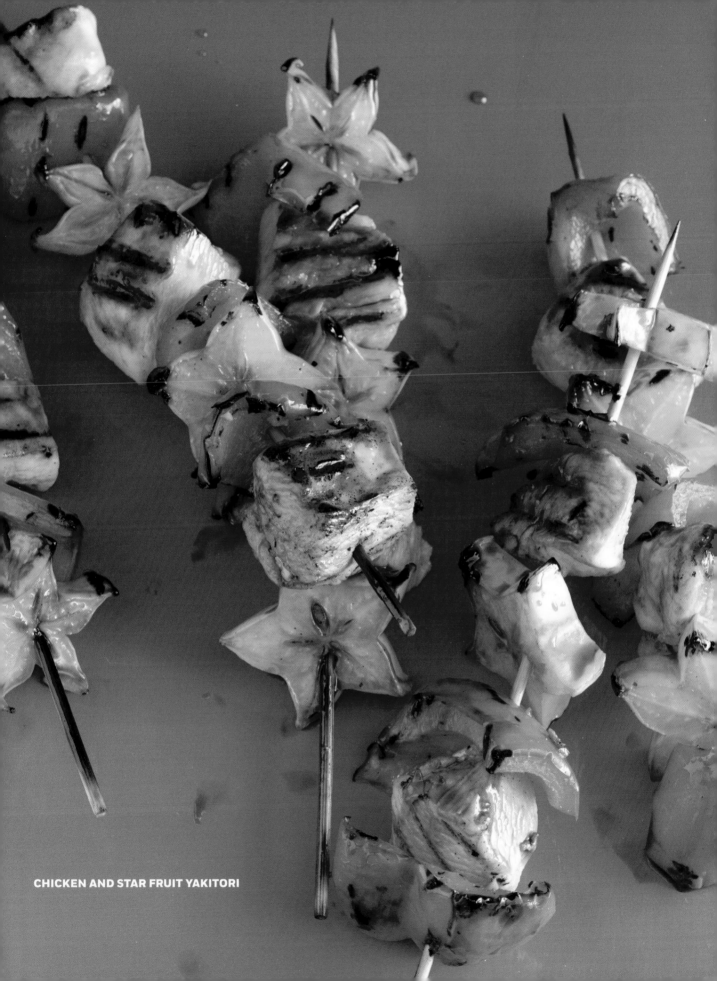

CHICKEN AND STAR FRUIT YAKITORI

little spinach triangles with dill and mint

SERVES 8

PER SERVING

▲ 1 (10-ounce) box frozen chopped spinach, thawed and squeezed dry

⅔ cup finely crumbled reduced-fat feta cheese

▲ 1 large egg white

▲ 3 scallions, chopped

2 tablespoons chopped fresh dill

2 tablespoons chopped fresh mint

¼ teaspoon black pepper

8 (12 x 16-inch) sheets phyllo dough, thawed if frozen

1 Preheat oven to 375°F. Lightly spray baking sheet with olive oil nonstick spray.

2 Stir together spinach, feta, egg white, scallions, dill, mint, and pepper in medium bowl until mixed well.

3 Set stack of phyllo sheets to one side. Keep covered with damp paper towels to prevent them from drying out.

4 Place 1 phyllo sheet, with long side facing you, on work surface and lightly spray with nonstick spray. Top with another sheet and lightly spray. With pizza cutter or knife, cut crosswise into 6 strips. Place scant tablespoonful of spinach mixture near end of each strip. Fold corner of phyllo over filling and continue to fold up flag-style, maintaining triangle shape. Transfer to prepared baking sheet and continue with remaining phyllo and filling, making total of 24 triangles. Lightly spray with nonstick spray.

5 Bake until phyllo is golden brown, about 25 minutes. Transfer to wire racks. Serve warm or at room temperature.

PER SERVING (*3 triangles*): 95 Cal, 3 g Total Fat, 1 g Sat Fat, 0 g Trans Fat, 3 mg Chol, 283 mg Sod, 12 g Carb, 0 g Sugar, 2 g Fib, 6 g Prot, 87 mg Calc.

shrimp summer rolls with sriracha dipping sauce

SERVES 8

⅓ cup lime juice

2 tablespoons sugar, preferably superfine

1 tablespoon Asian fish sauce

1 teaspoon Sriracha (hot chile sauce) or to taste

▲ 5 thin slices red chile pepper (optional)

8 (8-inch) rice-paper rounds

▲ 16 cooked large shrimp (about ½ pound), halved lengthwise

▲ 2 cups packaged coleslaw mix (from 10-ounce package)

▲ 1 cup matchstick-cut or coarsely grated carrots

¼ cup lightly packed fresh cilantro leaves

¼ cup lightly packed fresh mint leaves

¼ cup lightly packed fresh basil leaves

1 To make dipping sauce, whisk together lime juice, sugar, fish sauce, and Sriracha in serving bowl until sugar is dissolved. Add chile pepper slices, if using.

2 Soak rice-paper rounds, one at a time, in large bowl of hot water just until softened, 10–30 seconds. Place rounds, as they are softened, on double layer of paper towels to drain.

3 Lay softened wrappers out on work surface. Arrange 4 shrimp halves along center of each wrapper, leaving border at top and bottom; layer evenly with coleslaw mix, carrots, cilantro, mint, and basil. Fold in sides of wrappers, then roll up tightly to enclose filling. Cut each roll in half on diagonal and serve with dipping sauce. Rolls can be made up to 4 hours ahead. Place on damp paper towel–lined baking sheet, cover with damp towels, and wrap in plastic wrap.

PER SERVING (1 summer roll and about 1 tablespoon sauce): 66 Cal, 0 g Total Fat, 0 g Sat Fat, 0 g Trans Fat, 21 mg Chol, 222 mg Sod, 12 g Carb, 4 g Sugar, 1 g Fib, 4 g Prot, 24 mg Calc.

now try this

Sriracha is a chile-laced hot sauce that is as popular in Thailand as ketchup is in the U.S. It is made of chile peppers, distilled white vinegar, garlic, sugar, and salt. The brand of Sriracha most readily available is Huy Fong, which comes in a tall clear plastic bottle with a prominently displayed red rooster and a bright green top. Produced in California, it is found in supermarkets and on the tables of many Asian restaurants.

JALAPEÑO AND CILANTRO PICKLED SHRIMP

jalapeño and cilantro pickled shrimp

SERVES 4

- ▲ **1 pound cooked peeled and deveined medium shrimp, tails left on if desired**
- ▲ **½ orange bell pepper, finely diced**
- ▲ **1 plum tomato, chopped**
- ▲ **1 scallion, thinly sliced**
- ▲ **½ jalapeño pepper, seeded and minced**
- **¼ cup chopped fresh cilantro**
- **3 tablespoons lime juice**
- **1 tablespoon extra-virgin olive oil**
- **½ teaspoon ground cumin**
- ▲ **Small lettuce leaves, such as Bibb**

1 Combine all ingredients except lettuce in medium bowl and toss until mixed well. Cover and refrigerate at least 2 hours or up to 6 hours.

2 Line 4 glass dishes or plates with lettuce. Divide shrimp mixture among dishes.

PER SERVING (*1 cup shrimp salad*): 155 Cal, 5 g Total Fat, 1 g Sat Fat, 0 g Trans Fat, 221 mg Chol, 259 mg Sod, 3 g Carb, 1 g Sugar, 1 g Fib, 24 g Prot, 54 mg Calc.

for your info

Here's how to easily peel and devein shrimp: Starting at the head end, peel off the shell including the tail, if desired. With a small knife, make a cut along the back of each shrimp to expose the black vein (the intestinal tract), and pull it out.

garlicky italian-style clams

SERVES 6

3 PointsPlus value

PER SERVING

1 cup fresh whole wheat bread crumbs (about 2 slices bread)

½ cup finely chopped fresh parsley

1 tablespoon chopped fresh oregano

1 tablespoon chopped fresh mint

3 garlic cloves, minced

1 tablespoon water

2 teaspoons extra-virgin olive oil

¼ teaspoon black pepper

▲ **2 dozen littleneck clams, shucked and bottom shells reserved**

Lemon wedges

1 Preheat broiler.

2 Stir together bread crumbs, parsley, oregano, mint, garlic, water, oil, and pepper in small bowl until crumbs are evenly moistened, adding a bit of additional water, if needed.

3 Place 1 clam in each shell and top with heaping teaspoon of bread-crumb mixture. Arrange in broiler pan and lightly spray with olive oil nonstick spray. Broil 5 inches from heat until clams are cooked through and topping is golden and crispy, about 4 minutes. Serve with lemon wedges.

PER SERVING (*4 clams*): 149 Cal, 3 g Total Fat, 1 g Sat Fat, 0 g Trans Fat, 25 mg Chol, 265 mg Sod, 14 g Carb, 3 g Sugar, 1 g Fib, 13 g Prot, 99 mg Calc.

provençal baked mussels

SERVES 8

PointsPlus® value

PER SERVING

¼ cup plain dried whole wheat bread crumbs

3 tablespoons finely grated pecorino-romano cheese

▲ 2 tablespoons sun-dried tomatoes (not packed in oil), finely chopped

1 tablespoon chopped fresh parsley

2 large garlic cloves, minced

2 teaspoons extra-virgin olive oil

1½ teaspoons herbes de Provence

¼ teaspoon black pepper

▲ 16 mussels, scrubbed and debearded

1 Preheat oven to 425°F.

2 Stir together all ingredients except mussels in small bowl until bread crumbs are evenly moistened, adding a bit of water if needed.

3 Fill large saucepan with ½ inch of water and bring to boil over high heat; add mussels. Cook, covered, until mussels open, about 5 minutes; drain. Discard any mussels that do not open.

4 When mussels are cool enough to handle, remove and discard top half of each shell. Spoon heaping teaspoonful of bread-crumb mixture over each mussel; lightly spray with olive oil nonstick spray. Arrange mussels in shallow pan. Bake until topping is golden and crispy, about 5 minutes.

PER SERVING (*2 stuffed mussels*): 67 Cal, 3 g Total Fat, 1 g Sat Fat, 0 g Trans Fat, 12 mg Chol, 200 mg Sod, 4 g Carb, 1 g Sugar, 1 g Fib, 6 g Prot, 55 mg Calc.

now try this

Herbes de Provence is a blend of herbs native to southern France. The mix usually consists of basil, fennel, lavender, marjoram, rosemary, sage, and thyme. Herbes de Provence is often added to stews and other braised dishes, soups, and vegetables. It frequently comes packed in covered red clay crocks with decorative black writing.

roasted asparagus wrapped in lemon-basil prosciutto

SERVES 10

▲ **20 asparagus spears (about 1 pound), trimmed**

¼ teaspoon black pepper

10 very thin slices prosciutto (about 5 ounces), halved lengthwise

2 tablespoons chopped fresh basil

Finely grated zest of ½ lemon

1 Preheat oven to 400°F.

2 Put asparagus in jelly-roll pan and spray with olive oil nonstick spray; sprinkle with pepper and toss to coat evenly. Spread asparagus to form single layer. Roast until asparagus is tender, about 15 minutes. Let cool.

3 Lay slices of prosciutto on work surface. Mix together basil and lemon zest in cup; sprinkle over prosciutto. Tightly wrap 1 piece of prosciutto around each asparagus spear, exposing tip. Arrange on platter and serve.

PER SERVING (*2 asparagus*): 40 Cal, 2 g Total Fat, 1 g Sat Fat, 0 g Trans Fat, 11 mg Chol, 376 mg Sod, 2 g Carb, 1 g Sugar, 1 g Fib, 5 g Prot, 13 mg Calc.

zucchini–fresh basil frittata

SERVES 4

1 tablespoon olive oil

▲ 1 onion, chopped

3 garlic cloves, minced

▲ 2 zucchini, diced

▲ 1 red bell pepper, diced

▲ ½ cup cherry tomatoes, halved

⅓ cup lightly packed thinly sliced fresh basil

½ teaspoon salt

¼ teaspoon black pepper

▲ 1 (16-ounce) container fat-free egg substitute

1 Preheat broiler.

2 Heat oil in 10-inch ovenproof nonstick skillet over medium heat. Add onion and cook, stirring, until softened, about 5 minutes. Stir in garlic and cook, stirring, until fragrant, about 1 minute. Add zucchini, bell pepper, tomatoes, basil, salt, and pepper; cook, stirring, until vegetables are softened, about 6 minutes longer.

3 Pour egg substitute evenly over vegetable mixture. Cook, without stirring, until eggs are almost set, about 5 minutes. Place skillet 5 inches from heat and broil until frittata is set and top is golden, about 5 minutes longer. Slide frittata onto serving plate and cut into 4 wedges. Serve hot, warm, or at room temperature.

PER SERVING (*1 wedge*): 102 Cal, 4 g Total Fat, 1 g Sat Fat, 0 g Trans Fat, 0 mg Chol, 473 mg Sod, 7 g Total Carb, 3 g Total Sugar, 1 g Fib, 11 g Prot, 59 mg Calc.

Make this frittata a little heartier by sprinkling it with 4 ounces of crumbled fat-free feta cheese after adding the egg substitute in step 3. This will increase the per-serving *PointsPlus* value by *1*.

citrusy olives with sun-dried tomatoes and thyme

SERVES 12 • 20 MINUTES

2 PointsPlus® value

PER SERVING

½ pound (about 24) brine-cured green and/or black olives

2 (3-inch) strips orange zest

2 (3-inch) strips lemon zest

▲ 2 sun-dried tomatoes (not packed in oil), cut into strips

2 garlic cloves, lightly crushed with side of large knife

1 bay leaf

¾ teaspoon dried thyme

½ teaspoon extra-virgin olive oil

Generous pinch cayenne

1 Stir together all ingredients in medium bowl. Refrigerate, covered, at least 1 day or up to 1 week.

2 To serve, transfer olive mixture to serving bowl. Serve at room temperature.

PER SERVING (about 2 garnished olives): 57 Cal, 5 g Total Fat, 1 g Sat Fat, 0 g Trans Fat, 0 mg Chol, 315 mg Sod, 2 g Carb, 0 g Sugar, 0 g Fib, 1 g Prot, 8 mg Calc.

for your info

There are several different brine-cured olives that will work in this tasty dish, including Kalamata, niçoise, manzanilla, picholine, and sevillano.

HOT AND SPICY CASHEWS, p. 36

CITRUSY OLIVES WITH SUN-DRIED TOMATOES AND THYME

hot and spicy cashews

SERVES 16

PER SERVING

2 teaspoons coriander seeds

1 teaspoon cumin seeds

2 teaspoons smoked hot paprika

¾ teaspoon kosher salt

▲ **1 large egg white**

2 cups unsalted roasted cashews

1 Preheat oven to 300°F. Line large baking sheet with parchment paper.

2 Heat small heavy skillet over medium heat until hot but not smoking. Add coriander and cumin seeds; cook, stirring frequently, until fragrant and toasted, about 4 minutes. Transfer to plate and let cool completely. Finely grind spices in coffee grinder or spice grinder. Transfer to small bowl and stir in paprika and salt.

3 With electric mixer on medium-high speed, beat egg white in medium bowl until stiff peaks form when beaters are lifted, about 3 minutes. Reduce speed to low and beat in spice mixture. Add nuts; with rubber spatula, toss until nuts are coated.

4 Spread nuts on prepared baking sheet. Bake 15 minutes. With wide metal spatula, turn nuts over and separate. Bake until medium brown, about 15 minutes longer. Turn nuts over and separate; let cool completely on baking sheet on wire rack. (Nuts will crisp as they cool.) Break up any nuts that stick together. Store in airtight container up to 2 weeks.

PER SERVING (*about 10 nuts*)**:** 81 cal, 6 g Fat, 1 g Sat Fat, 0 g Trans Fat, 0 mg Chol, 77 mg Sod, 5 g Carb, 1 g Sugar, 1 g Fib, 2 g Prot, 0 mg Calc.

savory parmesan-walnut biscotti

MAKES 50

PER SERVING

1 cup + 3 tablespoons all-purpose flour

½ cup finely grated Parmesan cheese

¼ cup finely chopped walnuts

1 teaspoon baking powder

¾ teaspoon salt

⅛ teaspoon cayenne

▲ 1 large egg

▲ 1 large egg yolk

2 tablespoons low-fat (1%) milk

1½ teaspoons olive oil

1 Set racks in middle and lower third of oven and preheat to 350°F. Line large baking sheet with parchment paper.

2 Whisk together flour, Parmesan, walnuts, baking powder, salt, and cayenne in medium bowl. Whisk together egg, egg yolk, milk, and oil in small bowl until blended well. Stir egg mixture into flour mixture until sticky dough forms. On lightly floured work surface with floured hands, knead dough until thoroughly blended.

3 Divide dough into 2 equal pieces. Form each piece of dough into 10-inch log. Place logs on prepared baking sheet. Bake on middle rack until biscotti is firm when lightly pressed and browned on bottom, about 30 minutes, rotating baking sheet from front to back about halfway through baking time. Let cool on baking sheet on wire rack about 15 minutes.

4 Meanwhile, reduce oven temperature to 300°F.

5 With serrated knife, cut each log into 25 (⅜-inch) slices, making total of 50 slices. Place slices, cut side down, on one or two baking sheets; bake until lightly browned, about 20 minutes, rotating baking sheet halfway through baking time. Turn biscotti over and bake until lightly browned on second side, about 20 minutes longer. Transfer to racks and let cool completely.

PER SERVING (4 biscotti): 84 Cal, 4 g Total Fat, 1 g Sat Fat, 0 g Trans Fat, 28 mg Chol, 210 mg Sod, 8 g Carb, 0 g Sugar, 0 g Fib, 4 g Prot, 25 mg Calc.

To keep some biscotti on hand for later, wrap them in packets of four in plastic wrap, pack into a zip-close plastic freezer bag, and pop into the freezer. This way you won't be tempted to eat too many at a time, and they will stay fresh for several months.

tex-mex snack mix

SERVES 10

1½ tablespoons light stick butter

1 tablespoon packed brown sugar

1½ teaspoons Worcestershire sauce

1 teaspoon ground cumin

1 teaspoon hot pepper sauce or to taste

▲ 3 cups plain air-popped popcorn

2 cups corn cereal squares

1½ cups baked tortilla chips, broken into large pieces

1 cup unsalted pretzel sticks

¼ cup hulled pumpkin seeds

½ (1¼-ounce package) reduced-sodium taco seasoning mix

1 Preheat oven to 250°F. Spray medium roasting pan with nonstick spray.

2 Melt butter in small saucepan over low heat. Stir in brown sugar, Worcestershire sauce, cumin, and pepper sauce. Remove saucepan from heat.

3 Combine popcorn, cereal, tortilla chips, pretzels, and pumpkin seeds in prepared pan. Drizzle butter mixture over popcorn mixture and sprinkle with taco seasoning; toss until coated evenly. Spread to form even layer.

4 Bake, stirring occasionally, until mixture is crisp, about 45 minutes. Turn mixture out onto sheet of foil and let cool. Store in airtight container up to 1 week.

PER SERVING (½ cup): 161 Cal, 4 g Total Fat, 1 g Sat Fat, 0 g Trans Fat, 3 mg Chol, 304 mg Sod, 27 g Carb, 2 g Sugar, 1 g Fib, 4 g Prot, 41 mg Calc.

curried dried cherry popcorn

SERVES 8 • 20 MINUTES

1 tablespoon olive oil

2 teaspoons curry powder

▲ 6 cups plain air-popped popcorn

½ cup dried tart cherries

⅓ cup sunflower seeds

1 Stir together oil and curry powder in microwavable cup. Microwave on High until fragrant, about 1 minute.

2 Toss together popcorn, cherries, and sunflower seeds in serving bowl. Drizzle with curry oil and toss until coated evenly.

PER SERVING (¾ cup): 97 Cal, 5 g Total Fat, 1 g Sat Fat, 0 g Trans Fat, 0 mg Chol, 1 mg Sod, 13 g Carb, 4 g Sugar, 4 g Fib, 2 g Prot, 10 mg Calc.

for your info

There are basically two types of curry powder: sweet and hot. Curry powder is a blend of up to 20 spices, including cardamom, chiles, cinnamon, cloves, coriander, cumin, fennel, fenugreek, mace, nutmeg, red and black pepper, saffron, tamarind, and turmeric. Whether you use sweet or hot curry powder is simply a matter of personal preference. It is a good idea, however, to have both on hand.

chapter 2

light soups and salads

all-dressed-up cold beet soup

SERVES 6

▲ 1½ pounds medium beets, ends trimmed

6 cups water

2 tablespoons superfine sugar

1½ tablespoons lemon juice

¾ teaspoon salt

¼ teaspoon black pepper

¾ cup reduced-fat sour cream

▲ ¾ cup peeled, seeded, and diced cucumber

▲ 3 hard-cooked large egg whites, chopped

▲ ⅓ cup diced red onion

2 tablespoons snipped fresh dill

1 Combine beets and water in large saucepan; bring to boil. Reduce heat and simmer, covered, until beets are tender, about 40 minutes.

2 With slotted spoon, transfer beets to cutting board and let cool. Pour beet cooking liquid through fine-mesh sieve set over medium bowl. Reserve liquid. When beets are cool enough to handle, slip off skins. Cut half of beets into chunks.

3 Transfer about 2 cups of beet liquid to blender along with cut-up beets; blend until smooth. Add to beet liquid in bowl. Coarsely grate remaining whole beets and add to soup. Stir in sugar, lemon juice, salt, and pepper until sugar is dissolved. Cover and refrigerate until well chilled, about 4 hours or up to overnight.

4 Ladle soup into 6 bowls. Top each serving with dollop of sour cream; sprinkle evenly with cucumber, egg whites, onion, and dill.

PER SERVING (1½ cups soup and 2 tablespoons sour cream): 130 Cal, 5 g Total Fat, 3 g Sat Fat, 0 g Trans Fat, 11 mg Chol, 439 mg Sod, 18 g Carb, 11 g Sugar, 3 g Fib, 6 g Prot, 76 mg Calc.

for your info

The amount of time it takes for beets to cook depends on their size and age. Smaller and/or younger beets cook through in about 40 minutes, while larger and/or older beets can take up to 1 hour. To test for doneness, insert a toothpick into a beet. When it goes in easily, the beets are done.

ASPARAGUS VICHYSSOISE
WITH CHIVE FLOWERS

asparagus vichyssoise with chive flowers

SERVES 6

▲ **1 pound asparagus**

2 teaspoons olive oil

▲ **1 leek (white and light green part only), thinly sliced**

▲ **3 cups reduced-sodium vegetable broth**

▲ **1 (8-ounce) russet potato, peeled and cut into ½-inch pieces**

2 fresh thyme sprigs

¾ teaspoon salt

⅛ teaspoon pepper, preferably white

1 cup low-fat (1%) milk

2 teaspoons basil-flavored olive oil

4 chive flowers, crumbled, for garnish

1 Cut off tips from 18 asparagus spears and set aside for garnish; cut remaining asparagus into 2-inch lengths.

2 Bring medium saucepan of water to boil; add asparagus tips and cook until bright green, about 1 minute. Drain in colander, then rinse under cold running water and pat dry with paper towels.

3 Heat olive oil in large saucepan over medium heat. Add leek and cook, stirring, until softened, about 5 minutes. Add broth, asparagus spears, potato, thyme sprigs, salt, and pepper. Cover and bring to boil. Reduce heat and simmer, covered, until vegetables are fork-tender, about 20 minutes. Discard thyme sprigs. Let soup cool about 5 minutes.

4 Puree soup, in batches, in blender. Transfer to large bowl and stir in milk. Let cool to room temperature, then cover and refrigerate until thoroughly chilled, at least 4 hours or up to 2 days.

5 Ladle soup into 6 bowls. Drizzle evenly with basil oil; top each serving with asparagus tips and sprinkle with chive flowers.

PER SERVING (*1 cup*): 101 cal, 4 g Fat, 1 g Sat Fat, 0 g Trans Fat, 2 mg Chol, 383 mg Sod, 15 g Carb, 6 g Sugar, 3 g Fib, 4 g Prot, 91 mg Calc.

Deep lilac-colored **chive flowers** are an easy and tasty way to garnish soups, omelettes, salads, and other dishes, especially if they already contain snipped fresh chives. Chive plants bloom in the spring and last for a week or so. If you like, garnish the soup with coarsely ground pepper and additional asparagus stalks instead of the tips.

black mushroom hot and sour soup

SERVES 4

- ▲ 3 dried Chinese black mushrooms
- ▲ 2½ cups reduced-sodium chicken broth
- 1 tablespoon + ¾ teaspoon cornstarch
- ▲ 1 (5-ounce) skinless boneless chicken breast, thinly sliced crosswise
- 2 teaspoons reduced-sodium soy sauce
- ▲ 4 shiitake mushrooms, stems removed and caps thinly sliced
- ▲ ¼ pound firm reduced-fat tofu, cut into ½-inch cubes
- 1 tablespoon + 1½ teaspoons unseasoned rice vinegar
- 1 tablespoon minced peeled fresh ginger
- 1 teaspoon Asian (dark) sesame oil
- ½ teaspoon salt
- Generous ¼ teaspoon coarsely ground black pepper
- ▲ 1 large egg, lightly beaten
- ▲ Thinly sliced white part of 1 scallion

1 Put dried mushrooms in small bowl and add enough boiling water to cover. Let stand until softened, about 30 minutes. Drain; snip off mushroom stems and discard. Rinse caps under cool running water and thinly slice. Set aside.

2 Stir together 2 tablespoons of broth and ¾ teaspoon of cornstarch in medium bowl until smooth. Add chicken and 1 teaspoon of soy sauce; stir until chicken is coated. Stir together 2 tablespoons broth and remaining 1 tablespoon cornstarch in cup until smooth.

3 Bring remaining 2¼ cups broth to boil in Dutch oven. Add chicken mixture and dried and fresh mushrooms; return to boil. Reduce heat and simmer, stirring occasionally, 1 minute. Add tofu and remaining 1 teaspoon soy sauce; return to boil, stirring occasionally. Re-stir cornstarch mixture in cup; stir into soup and cook, stirring constantly, until soup bubbles and thickens, about 30 seconds. Stir in vinegar, ginger, sesame oil, salt, and pepper.

4 Remove Dutch oven from heat; add egg in slow, steady stream, stirring soup once clockwise. Ladle soup into 4 bowls and sprinkle evenly with scallion.

PER SERVING (1 cup): 137 Cal, 5 g Total Fat, 1 g Sat Fat, 0 g Trans Fat, 73 mg Chol, 334 mg Sod, 10 g Carb, 1 g Sugar, 1 g Fib, 15 g Prot, 72 mg Calc.

microwaved fresh mint and pea soup

SERVES 4

3 PointsPlus value

PER SERVING

- ▲ 1 onion, chopped
- ▲ 2 celery stalks, thinly sliced
-   1 large garlic clove, minced
-   2 teaspoons olive oil
- ▲ 1 (10-ounce) box frozen baby peas
- ▲ 1 (32-ounce) carton unsalted chicken broth
- ▲ ¼ cup fat-free half-and-half
-   ⅓ cup lightly packed fresh mint leaves + thinly sliced leaves for garnish
-   ½ teaspoon salt
-   ¼ teaspoon black pepper

1 Combine onion, celery, garlic, and oil in large microwavable bowl. Cover with plastic wrap and vent one corner. Microwave on High until onion is softened, about 5 minutes. Add peas and broth. Microwave, covered, on High until peas are tender and soup is beginning to boil, about 5 minutes longer. Stir in half-and-half, whole mint leaves, salt, and pepper. Let cool about 5 minutes.

2 Puree soup, in batches, in blender. If serving hot, transfer to large saucepan and gently reheat. Or refrigerate, covered, to serve chilled. To serve, ladle soup into 4 bowls. Top each serving with sprinkling of sliced mint.

PER SERVING (*about 1¼ cups*): 153 Cal, 4 g Total Fat, 1 g Sat Fat, 0 g Trans Fat, 24 mg Chol, 469 mg Sod, 17 g Carb, 5 g Sugar, 5 g Fib, 11 g Prot, 66 mg Calc.

stay on track

Loaded with flavor and fiber, this perfect-for-spring soup can be made even silkier by adding refrigerated diced cooked potato to the blender and pureeing it with the soup in step 2 (6 ounces of cooked potato will increase the per-serving *PointsPlus* value by *1*).

thai lemongrass-coconut soup

SERVES 6

▲ **½ pound shiitake mushrooms, stems removed and caps thinly sliced**

▲ **1 small red bell pepper, diced**

▲ **2 carrots, thinly sliced**

3 lemongrass stalks, chopped, or finely grated zest of 1 lime

▲ **1 (32-ounce) container reduced-sodium vegetable broth**

1 cup water

¼ teaspoon cayenne or to taste

¾ cup light (reduced-fat) coconut milk

¾ cup lightly packed fresh cilantro leaves

1 tablespoon + 1 teaspoon lime juice

2 teaspoons Asian fish sauce

▲ **1 tomato, chopped**

▲ **4 scallions, thinly sliced on diagonal**

1 Combine mushrooms, bell pepper, carrots, lemongrass, broth, water, and cayenne in large saucepan; bring to boil. Reduce heat and simmer until vegetables are softened, about 10 minutes.

2 Stir coconut milk into saucepan and bring just to simmer. Remove saucepan from heat. Stir in half of cilantro, the lime juice, and fish sauce. Ladle soup into 6 bowls. Top each serving evenly with tomato, scallions, and remaining cilantro.

PER SERVING (*about 1¼ cups*): 74 Cal, 2 g Total Fat, 0 g Sat Fat, 0 g Trans Fat, 0 mg Chol, 268 mg Sod, 14 g Carb, 5 g Sugar, 3 g Fib, 2 g Prot, 36 mg Calc.

now try this

Lemongrass, an herb with a slender woody stem and lemon-mint flavor, is revered in Thai and Vietnamese cooking. It is found in some supermarkets, specialty food stores, and Asian markets. Choose stalks that are blemish-free and fresh looking. Tightly wrapped in plastic wrap, lemongrass can be stored in the refrigerator up to 2 weeks. To use it, strip away the tough outer leaves of the stalk and chop the tender inner stalk.

farmers' market roasted corn and potato soup

SERVES 6

- ▲ **6 ears of corn, husks and silk intact**
- **3 large garlic cloves, unpeeled**
- ▲ **1 russet potato (½ pound), peeled and cut into chunks**
- **3 cups cold water**
- ▲ **1 (14½-ounce) can reduced-sodium chicken broth**
- **2 teaspoons fresh thyme leaves**
- **¾ teaspoon salt**
- **¼ teaspoon black pepper**
- ▲ **½ cup fat-free half-and-half**
- **Snipped fresh chives for garnish**

1 Preheat oven to 425°F.

2 Place unhusked corn and garlic on baking sheet; roast until corn is fragrant and husks are lightly browned, about 25 minutes. Let corn and garlic cool.

3 When corn is cool enough to handle, remove husks and silk. Cut kernels from cobs. Cut 3 cobs in half; discard remaining cobs. Squeeze garlic pulp from peel.

4 Put reserved cobs, the corn kernels, potato, garlic pulp, water, broth, thyme, salt, and pepper in large pot and bring to boil. Reduce heat and simmer, covered, until potato is tender, about 20 minutes. Discard corn cobs. Let soup cool 5 minutes.

5 With slotted spoon, transfer corn kernels, potato, garlic pulp, and about 1½ cups of soup liquid to blender; blend until almost smooth, adding more liquid if needed. Return corn mixture to pot. Stir in half-and-half and gently reheat. Ladle soup into 6 bowls and sprinkle with chives.

PER SERVING (1¼ cups): 183 Cal, 2 g Total Fat, 0 g Sat Fat, 0 g Trans Fat, 0 mg Chol, 355 mg Sod, 38 g Carb, 6 g Sugar, 5 g Fib, 7 g Prot, 43 mg Calc.

carrot soup with miso and sesame oil

SERVES 4

3 PointsPlus® value

PER SERVING

2 teaspoons canola oil

▲ 1 red onion, finely chopped

3 (3-inch strips) orange zest

2 garlic cloves, minced

1½ teaspoons minced peeled fresh ginger

⅛ teaspoon salt

▲ 1 (32-ounce) container reduced-sodium vegetable broth

▲ 1 pound carrots, coarsely grated

1 tablespoon white miso paste

1 teaspoon Asian (dark) sesame oil

▲ 2 scallions, sliced

1 Heat canola oil in large saucepan over medium heat. Add onion and cook, stirring, until softened, about 5 minutes. Add 2 strips of orange zest, the garlic, ginger, and salt; cook, stirring constantly, until fragrant, about 30 seconds.

2 Add broth and carrots to saucepan; bring to boil. Reduce heat and simmer, covered, stirring occasionally, until carrots are fork-tender, about 30 minutes.

3 Let soup cool 5 minutes. Puree soup, in batches, in blender, returning soup to saucepan. Whisk together ½ cup of soup and the miso in small bowl until smooth; whisk back into soup.

4 Very thinly slice remaining strip of orange zest. Ladle soup into 4 bowls; drizzle evenly with sesame oil and sprinkle with scallions and zest.

PER SERVING (1¼ *cups*): 116 cal, 4 g Fat, 0 g Sat Fat, 0 g Trans Fat, 0 mg Chol, 429 mg Sod, 19 g Carb, 9 g Sugar, 6 g Fib, 2 g Prot, 72 mg Calc.

stay on track

Add some satisfying crunch *and* keep the *PointsPlus* value low by topping the soup with jumbo whole wheat croutons (1 slice of cut up toasted whole wheat bread per serving will increase the *PointsPlus* value by *2*).

creamy peanut butter soup with ginger and chile

SERVES 4

PER SERVING

½ teaspoon canola oil

▲ 1 red bell pepper, chopped

▲ 1 small onion, chopped

2 teaspoons minced peeled fresh ginger

1 large garlic clove, minced

▲ 1 (32-ounce) carton reduced-sodium chicken broth

▲ ½ (14½-ounce) can diced tomatoes

¼ cup reduced-fat creamy peanut butter

1½ teaspoons chili powder or to taste

⅛ teaspoon salt

▲ 1 plum tomato, seeded and diced

▲ ½ thinly sliced jalapeño pepper

1 Coat large pot with oil and set over medium heat. Add bell pepper, onion, ginger, and garlic; cook, stirring, until vegetables are softened, about 5 minutes. Stir in broth, canned tomatoes, peanut butter, chili powder, and salt; bring to boil. Reduce heat and simmer, covered, stirring occasionally, until vegetables are very soft, about 20 minutes.

2 Remove pot from heat; let soup cool 5 minutes. Puree soup, in batches, in blender. Return soup to pot and gently reheat. Ladle soup into 4 bowls. Sprinkle evenly with fresh tomato and jalapeño.

PER SERVING (*about 1½ cups*): 167 Cal, 8 g Total Fat, 2 g Sat Fat, 0 g Trans Fat, 0 mg Chol, 393 mg Sod, 17 g Carb, 7 g Sugar, 3 g Fib, 10 g Prot, 29 mg Calc.

sweet potato soup with coconut, cilantro, and lime

SERVES 6

1 tablespoon olive oil

▲ 1 onion, chopped

▲ 1 (32-ounce) container reduced-sodium chicken broth

▲ 1¼ pounds sweet potatoes, peeled and cut into chunks

2 tablespoons coarsely chopped peeled fresh ginger

2 tablespoons packed light brown sugar

¾ teaspoon ground cardamom

¾ teaspoon salt

¼ teaspoon ground nutmeg

¼ teaspoon red pepper flakes

¼ cup light (reduced-fat) coconut milk

Finely grated zest and juice of ½ lime

3 tablespoons chopped fresh cilantro

3 tablespoons dried unsweetened coconut shavings, toasted

1 Heat oil in nonstick Dutch oven over medium heat. Add onion and cook, stirring, until softened, about 5 minutes. Add broth, potatoes, ginger, brown sugar, cardamom, salt, nutmeg, and pepper flakes; bring to boil. Reduce heat and simmer, partially covered, until potatoes are fork-tender, about 20 minutes.

2 Let soup cool 5 minutes. Puree soup, in batches, in blender. Return soup to pot. Stir in coconut milk and lime zest and juice; gently reheat. Ladle soup into 6 bowls. Sprinkle evenly with cilantro and coconut shavings.

PER SERVING (*about 1 cup*): 151 Cal, 5 g Total Fat, 2 g Sat Fat, 0 g Trans Fat, 0 mg Chol, 329 mg Sod, 23 g Carb, 8 g Sugar, 3 g Fib, 5 g Prot, 37 mg Calc.

for your info

Unsweetened coconut shavings are sold in health food stores. These larger flakes are more dramatic looking than flaked sweetened coconut, making them an ideal garnish for soups and salads. To toast, spread the coconut in a small baking pan and bake in the oven or toaster oven at 350°F, stirring, until golden, about 5 minutes.

CREAMY TOMATO-APPLE SOUP
AND SPICY PEPPER AND ONION
STEAK SANDWICHES, p.83

creamy tomato-apple soup

SERVES 4

▲ **5 small red apples (about 1 pound), unpeeled**

1 tablespoon olive oil

▲ **3 celery stalks including leaves, stalks coarsely chopped and leaves reserved**

▲ **1 small onion, coarsely chopped**

1 teaspoon coriander seeds

¼ teaspoon ground ginger

¼ teaspoon salt

¼ teaspoon black pepper

▲ **1 (32-ounce) carton reduced-sodium chicken broth**

▲ **1 (14½-ounce) can diced tomatoes**

1 Core and coarsely chop 4 apples.

2 Heat oil in Dutch oven over medium heat. Add chopped apples, chopped celery, onion, coriander seeds, ginger, salt, and pepper; cook, stirring, until vegetables are softened, about 5 minutes. Stir in broth and tomatoes; bring to boil. Reduce heat and simmer, covered, until vegetables are fork-tender, about 20 minutes.

3 Let soup cool 5 minutes. Puree soup, in batches, in blender. Pour through fine sieve set over large bowl, pressing hard on solids to extract as much liquid as possible. Discard solids.

4 Thinly slice remaining apple. Ladle soup into 4 bowls and top each serving with celery leaves and sliced apple.

PER SERVING (1½ *cups*): 204 cal, 5 g Fat, 1 g Sat Fat, 0 g Trans Fat, 0 mg Chol, 494 mg Sod, 37 g Carb, 24 g Sugar, 7 g Fib, 6 g Prot, 60 mg Calc.

truffle salt–dusted potato-leek soup

SERVES 4

1 tablespoon olive oil

▲ 1 large leek (white and light green part only), chopped

1 large garlic clove, minced

▲ 4 Yukon Gold potatoes, peeled and cut into chunks

▲ 1 (32-ounce) carton unsalted chicken broth

▲ 1 cup fat-free half-and-half

2 tablespoons finely chopped fresh parsley

⅛ teaspoon black pepper

¾ teaspoon black truffle sea salt or plain coarse sea salt

1 Heat oil in large saucepan over medium heat. Add leek and garlic; cook, stirring, until softened, about 5 minutes. Add potatoes and broth; bring to boil. Reduce heat and simmer, covered, until potatoes are tender, about 15 minutes; let cool 5 minutes.

2 Puree soup, in batches, in blender. Return soup to saucepan and stir in half-and-half, parsley, and pepper. Gently reheat. Ladle soup into 4 bowls and sprinkle evenly with truffle salt.

PER SERVING (*about 1 cup*): 222 Cal, 5 g Total Fat, 1 g Sat Fat, 0 g Trans Fat, 0 mg Chol, 561 mg Sod, 38 g Carb, 8 g Sugar, 4 g Fib, 11 g Prot, 127 mg Calc.

slow-cooker minestrone with pasta and parmesan

SERVES 8

4 PointsPlus© value

PER SERVING

- ▲ 1 (15½-ounce) can red kidney beans, rinsed and drained
- ▲ 1 (14½-ounce) can diced tomatoes
- 7 cups water
- ▲ 2 carrots, diced
- ▲ 2 onions, diced
- ▲ 2 zucchini, quartered lengthwise and sliced
- ▲ ½ pound green beans, trimmed and cut into 1-inch pieces
- 3 garlic cloves, minced
- ¾ teaspoon salt
- ¼ teaspoon black pepper
- 1 cup small pasta, such as tubettini or orzo
- ▲ 1 bunch baby spinach
- ⅓ cup chopped fresh basil
- ½ cup finely grated Parmesan cheese

1 Combine kidney beans, tomatoes, water, carrots, onions, zucchini, green beans, garlic, salt, and pepper in 5- or 6-quart slow cooker. Cover and cook until vegetables are fork-tender, 4–5 hours on high or 8–10 hours on low.

2 About 30 minutes before cooking time is up, cook pasta according to package directions, omitting salt if desired. Drain pasta and stir into soup along with spinach and basil. Serve with Parmesan.

PER SERVING (1½ *cups*): 188 Cal, 2 g Total Fat, 1 g Sat Fat, 0 g Trans Fat, 4 mg Chol, 445 mg Sod, 34 g Carb, 7 g Sugar, 9 g Fib, 10 g Prot, 115 mg Calc.

stay on track

Adding finely shredded green cabbage to this minestrone soup along with the other vegetables in step 1 makes it even more authentic without increasing the *PointsPlus* value.

saffron-scented monkfish soup with bread toasts

SERVES 4

PER SERVING

1 tablespoon olive oil

▲ 1 onion, chopped

▲ ½ small fennel bulb, chopped

3 large garlic cloves, minced

▲ 2 tomatoes, chopped

3 tablespoons licorice liqueur, such as Pernod or anisette

2 (3-inch) strips orange zest

1 (32-ounce) carton seafood broth or 4 (8-ounce) bottles clam juice

½ teaspoon saffron threads, crushed

1 teaspoon herbes de Provence (see tip page 31)

▲ 1 pound monkfish or halibut fillet, cut into 1-inch chunks

4 (½-inch) slices whole wheat baguette, toasted

1 Heat oil in nonstick Dutch oven over medium heat. Add onion, fennel, and garlic; cook, stirring, until onion is golden, about 8 minutes. Add tomatoes, Pernod, and orange zest; cook, stirring occasionally, until tomatoes are softened, about 4 minutes.

2 Stir broth, saffron, and herbes de Provence into pot; bring to boil. Reduce heat and simmer until flavors are blended, about 10 minutes longer.

3 Add monkfish to soup and bring to simmer; cook, covered, until fish is just opaque in center, about 5 minutes. Ladle soup into 4 bowls. Serve with toast.

PER SERVING (*2 cups*): 260 Cal, 6 g Total Fat, 1 g Sat Fat, 0 g Trans Fat, 35 mg Chol, 683 mg Sod, 27 g Carb, 6 g Sugar, 4 g Fib, 23 g Prot, 74 mg Calc.

stay on track

Keep the *PointsPlus* value the same while turning this soup into a complete meal. Start off with a vitamin-packed mixed greens and tomato salad dressed with balsamic vinegar and end with a bowl of freshly cut fruit sprinkled with thinly sliced fresh mint.

**SAFFRON-SCENTED MONKFISH
SOUP WITH BREAD TOASTS**

moroccan chickpea soup

SERVES 6

PER SERVING

1 tablespoon olive oil

▲ 4 small red onions, thinly sliced

2 teaspoons ground coriander

1½ teaspoons ground ginger

1 teaspoon ground cumin

1 teaspoon black pepper

▲ 6 cups reduced-sodium vegetable broth

▲ 1 (28-ounce) can whole peeled tomatoes, drained and chopped

▲ 1 (15½-ounce) can chickpeas, rinsed and drained

▲ ¾ cup brown lentils, picked over, rinsed, and drained

1¼ cups lightly packed fresh cilantro leaves

1 tablespoon lemon juice

Hot pepper sauce for serving

1 Heat oil in Dutch oven over medium heat. Add onions and cook, stirring, until softened, about 5 minutes. Stir in coriander, ginger, cumin, and black pepper; cook, stirring constantly, until fragrant, about 30 seconds.

2 Add broth, tomatoes, chickpeas, and lentils to pot; bring to boil. Reduce heat and simmer, covered, until lentils are tender, about 35 minutes. Remove Dutch oven from heat; stir in cilantro and lemon juice. Ladle soup into 6 bowls. Serve with hot sauce.

PER SERVING (1⅔ cups): 219 cal, 4 g Fat, 0 g Sat Fat, 0 g Trans Fat, 0 mg Chol, 592 mg Sod, 37 g Carb, 9 g Sugar, 9 g Fib, 10 g Prot, 80 mg Calc.

texas hill country caesar salad

SERVES 6

▲ **2 small poblano peppers**

⅓ cup reduced-fat mayonnaise

Finely grated zest of 1 lime

2–3 tablespoons lime juice

2 garlic cloves, minced

2 teaspoons Dijon mustard

¼ teaspoon salt

¼ teaspoon black pepper

6 tablespoons finely crumbled Cotija cheese

▲ **3 romaine lettuce hearts, thickly sliced**

½ cup lightly packed fresh cilantro leaves

18 baked tortilla chips, preferably blue corn, coarsely broken

1 To roast poblanos, preheat broiler. Put peppers on broiler rack and broil 5 inches from heat, turning, until charred on all sides, about 10 minutes. Transfer peppers to large zip-close plastic bag and seal; let steam 10 minutes. When cool enough to handle, peel off charred skin and remove stems and seeds. Cut poblanos into ½-inch pieces.

2 To make dressing, whisk together mayonnaise, lime zest and juice, garlic, mustard, salt, and black pepper. Stir in Cotija.

3 Combine romaine, cilantro, and poblanos in serving bowl. Top with dressing and toss until coated evenly. Divide salad among 6 plates and sprinkle evenly with tortilla chips.

PER SERVING (*about 2 cups*): 96 Cal, 4 g Total Fat, 2 g Sat Fat, 0 g Trans Fat, 5 mg Chol, 382 mg Sod, 12 g Carb, 2 g Sugar, 2 g Fib, 4 g Prot, 93 mg Calc.

now try this

Cotija (KO-tee-hah), also known as *Queso Añejado,* meaning "aged cheese," is a dry, crumbly cow's milk cheese that can be grated or crumbled. Parmesan is a good substitute.

crunchy apple, pomegranate, and greens salad

SERVES 4 • 20 MINUTES

PER SERVING

- ▲ **1 head Bibb or Boston lettuce, cut into bite-size pieces**
- ▲ **1 head Belgian endive, sliced**
- ▲ **1 Winesap, Macoun, or Golden Delicious apple, unpeeled, cored and thinly sliced**
- ▲ **1 small fennel bulb, halved and thinly sliced**
- ▲ **½ cup lightly packed mâche or baby spinach**
- **2 tablespoons champagne vinegar or cider vinegar**
- **1 tablespoon extra-virgin olive oil**
- **1 teaspoon honey**
- **½ teaspoon salt**
- **¼ teaspoon black pepper**
- **¼ cup pomegranate seeds**

1 Combine lettuce, endive, apple, fennel, and mâche in salad bowl.

2 To make dressing, whisk together vinegar, oil, honey, salt, and pepper in small bowl. Drizzle dressing over salad and toss until coated evenly. Sprinkle with pomegranate seeds.

PER SERVING (*scant 2 cups*): 110 Cal, 5 g Total Fat, 0 g Sat Fat, 0 g Trans Fat, 0 mg Chol, 344 mg Sod, 18 g Carb, 9 g Sugar, 7 g Fib, 3 g Prot, 102 mg Calc.

crisp iceberg lettuce wedges with chipotle–blue cheese dressing

SERVES 4

▲ **1 small head iceberg lettuce**

½ cup crumbled reduced-fat blue cheese

⅓ cup reduced-fat sour cream

3 tablespoons fat-free mayonnaise

½ canned chipotle pepper in adobo, minced

2 tablespoons red-wine vinegar

1 garlic clove, minced

¼ teaspoon salt

⅛ teaspoon black pepper

▲ **3 Kumato or plum tomatoes, diced**

▲ **3 scallions, thinly sliced**

1 Remove core from lettuce; gently rinse under cool running water and shake dry. Cut into 8 wedges. Wrap lettuce in paper towels; place in large zip-close plastic bag and refrigerate at least 1 hour or up to 8 hours to crisp.

2 To make dressing, stir together blue cheese, sour cream, mayonnaise, chipotle, vinegar, garlic, salt, and black pepper in small bowl.

3 Arrange 2 lettuce wedges on each of 4 plates. Spoon dressing evenly over and sprinkle with tomatoes and scallions.

PER SERVING (*1 plate*): 116 Cal, 6 g Total Fat, 5 g Sat Fat, 0 g Trans Fat, 18 mg Chol, 227 mg Sod, 9 g Carb, 5 g Sugar, 1 g Fib, 8 g Prot, 159 mg Calc.

now try this

Kumato tomatoes range in size from small to medium and in color from dark brown to golden brown. Unlike other tomatoes, which ripen from the outside in, Kumatos ripen from the inside out, which prevents them from getting soft spots while still unripe on the inside. When sliced open, expect a very juicy, silky texture and lots of great tomato flavor. Look for Kumatos in supermarkets, organic supermarkets, and specialty food stores.

georgia peach and endive salad with marcona almonds

SERVES 4

- ▲ **2 heads Belgian endive, thinly sliced**
- ▲ **2 peaches, halved, pitted, and cut into wedges**
- **3 tablespoons warm water**
- **1 tablespoon champagne vinegar or cider vinegar**
- **2 teaspoons extra-virgin olive oil**
- **2 teaspoons country-style Dijon mustard**
- **2 teaspoons chopped fresh thyme**
- **¼ teaspoon salt**
- **¼ teaspoon black pepper**
- ▲ **2 cups lightly packed baby greens, such as purple mustard greens or arugula**
- **¼ cup marcona or blanched whole regular almonds, chopped**
- ▲ **¼ cup crumbled fat-free feta cheese**

1 Combine endive and peaches in medium bowl.

2 To make dressing, whisk together water, vinegar, oil, mustard, thyme, salt, and pepper in small bowl. Drizzle over endive and peaches; toss until coated evenly.

3 Divide greens among 4 plates. Top evenly with peach-endive mixture and sprinkle evenly with almonds and feta.

PER SERVING (*about 1¼ cups*): 151 Cal, 7 g Total Fat, 1 g Sat Fat, 0 g Trans Fat, 1 mg Chol, 330 mg Sod, 17 g Carb, 1 g Sugar, 10 g Fib, 8 g Prot, 201 mg Calc.

Marcona almonds are a variety of almonds that are very popular in Spain, especially in tapas bars where they are served lightly fried and salted. They are rounder than standard almonds with a slightly softer texture and a richer, sweeter flavor. Marcona almonds are rather pricey; look for them in specialty food stores.

GEORGIA PEACH AND
ENDIVE SALAD WITH
MARCONA ALMONDS AND
MICROWAVED FRESH MINT
AND PEA SOUP, p.47

red and green salad with charred pecans and pepperoni bits

SERVES 6

- **3 tablespoons pecans, chopped**
- **20 slices turkey pepperoni, chopped**
- **1 tablespoon extra-virgin olive oil**
- **1 tablespoon white balsamic vinegar**
- **1 tablespoon water**
- **1 teaspoon Dijon mustard**
- **1 garlic clove, minced**
- **¼ teaspoon black pepper**
- ▲ **1 (5-ounce) package baby arugula**
- ▲ **1 head treviso radicchio or small head round radicchio, thinly sliced**

1 Spread pecans in medium nonstick skillet and set over medium heat. Cook, stirring occasionally, until lightly charred in spots, about 6 minutes; transfer to plate.

2 Add pepperoni to skillet and cook, stirring, until browned and crispy, about 6 minutes. Transfer to paper towels to drain.

3 To make dressing, whisk together oil, vinegar, water, mustard, garlic, and pepper in salad bowl. Add arugula and radicchio; toss until coated evenly. Sprinkle with pecans and pepperoni.

PER SERVING (2 cups): 81 Cal, 6 g Total Fat, 1 g Sat Fat, 0 g Trans Fat, 15 mg Chol, 247 mg Sod, 3 g Carb, 1 g Sugar, 1 g Fib, 5 g Prot, 45 mg Calc.

mixed salad with ginger-miso dressing

SERVES 4 • 20 MINUTES

2 tablespoons unseasoned rice vinegar

2 tablespoons reduced-sodium soy sauce

1 tablespoon Asian (dark) sesame oil

▲ 1 tablespoon chopped celery

▲ 1 tablespoon chopped onion

1 tablespoon grated peeled fresh ginger

1 teaspoon sugar

1 teaspoon white miso paste

Few drops hot pepper sauce

▲ 6 cups chopped romaine lettuce

▲ 2 mini cucumbers, thinly sliced

▲ 1 carrot, finely grated

▲ 12 cherry tomatoes, halved

1 To make dressing, combine vinegar, soy sauce, oil, celery, onion, ginger, sugar, miso, and pepper sauce in blender; blend until smooth.

2 Combine romaine, cucumbers, carrot, and tomatoes in salad bowl; toss until mixed. Drizzle with dressing and toss until coated evenly.

PER SERVING (about 1¾ cups): 74 Cal, 4 g Total Fat, 1 g Sat Fat, 0 g Trans Fat, 0 mg Chol, 343 mg Sod, 9 g Carb, 0 g Sugar, 5 g Fib, 2 g Prot, 43 mg Calc.

stay on track

This Japanese-inspired salad is anything but boring and contains good-for-you fiber and vitamins. Make it even more nutritious by adding several stalks of thinly sliced celery to the salad mixture.

celery-parmesan salad with lemon-anchovy dressing

SERVES 4

PER SERVING

- ▲ **4 cups very thin diagonally sliced celery**
- ▲ **1 red apple, unpeeled, cored and cut into ½-inch dice**
- **¼ cup lightly packed fresh flat-leaf parsley leaves**
- **2 tablespoons snipped fresh chives**
- **Finely grated zest and juice of 1 lemon**
- **1 tablespoon extra-virgin olive oil**
- **2 teaspoons Dijon mustard**
- **¾ teaspoon salt**
- **½ teaspoon anchovy paste**
- **¼ teaspoon black pepper**
- **¼ cup finely grated Parmesan cheese**

1 Combine celery, apple, parsley, and chives in large bowl.

2 To make dressing, whisk together lemon zest and juice, oil, mustard, salt, anchovy paste, and pepper in small bowl until blended.

3 Pour dressing over celery-apple mixture and toss until coated evenly. Divide salad among 4 plates and sprinkle evenly with Parmesan.

PER SERVING (*about 1¼ cups*): 102 Cal, 5 g Total Fat, 1 g Sat Fat, 0 g Trans Fat, 7 mg Chol, 406 mg Sod, 12 g Carb, 7 g Sugar, 3 g Fib, 3 g Prot, 111 mg Calc.

stay on track

Loaded with both flavor and crunch, this salad is sure to become part of your recipe repertoire. Make it even more enticing without increasing the *PointsPlus* value by adding 1 small fresh fennel bulb, thinly sliced, to the celery mixture in step 1.

thai-style broccoli salad

SERVES 4 • 20 MINUTES

2 PointsPlus® value

PER SERVING

- ▲ 10 green beans, trimmed and cut into 1-inch lengths
- 2 garlic cloves, coarsely chopped
- ▲ ½–1 jalapeño pepper, minced
- ▲ 2 cups packaged broccoli slaw
- 1 tablespoon Asian fish sauce
- 1 tablespoon lime juice
- 1 tablespoon packed brown sugar
- ▲ 8 cherry or grape tomatoes, halved or quartered
- 2 tablespoons unsalted roasted peanuts

PER SERVING (½ cup): 71 cal, 3 g Fat, 0 g Sat Fat, 0 g Trans Fat, 0 mg Chol, 366 mg Sod, 11 g Carb, 6 g Sugar, 3 g Fib, 3 g Prot, 40 mg Calc.

1 Bring small saucepan of water to boil. Add green beans and cook, covered, until crisp-tender, about 4 minutes. Drain in colander; rinse under cold running water and pat dry with paper towels.

2 Combine garlic and jalapeño in mini food processor; process until it forms a paste. Transfer to medium bowl; add broccoli slaw, beans, fish sauce, lime juice, and brown sugar. With clean hands, mix ingredients, squeezing them until wilted.

3 Add tomatoes and peanuts to slaw mixture and mix, gently squeezing ingredients until combined. Transfer to serving bowl. Serve at room temperature.

green bean, red onion, and tomato salad with ricotta salata

SERVES 6

▲ **1 pound slender green beans (haricots verts), trimmed**

▲ **½ pound plum tomatoes, chopped**

▲ **3 mini cucumbers, thinly sliced**

▲ **1 red onion, thinly sliced**

¼ cup lightly packed small fresh mint leaves

Finely grated zest and juice of 1 lemon

1 tablespoon extra-virgin olive oil

½ teaspoon salt

¼ teaspoon black pepper

⅓ cup coarsely grated ricotta salata or feta cheese

1 Bring large saucepan of lightly salted water to boil. Add green beans; return to boil and cook 4 minutes. Drain beans; rinse under cool running water and drain again.

2 Combine green beans, tomatoes, cucumbers, onion, mint, lemon zest and juice, oil, salt, and pepper in serving bowl. Toss until coated evenly. Sprinkle with ricotta salata.

PER SERVING (*about 1 cup*): 88 Cal, 4 g Fat, 2 g Sat Fat, 0 g Trans Fat, 7 mg Chol, 295 mg Sod, 11 g Carb, 4 g Sugar, 4 g Fib, 3 g Prot, 89 mg Calc.

classic chopped salad with zesty russian dressing

SERVES 6

- ½ cup fat-free mayonnaise
- ▲ ½ cup plain fat-free yogurt
- ¼ cup sweet pickle relish
- ¼ cup ketchup
- 2 teaspoons Worcestershire sauce
- 1½ teaspoons celery seeds
- ¼ teaspoon black pepper
- ▲ 4 large leaves green leaf lettuce
- ▲ 1 cup canned chickpeas, rinsed and drained
- ▲ 2 celery stalks, cut into ½-inch dice
- ▲ 1 large tomato, seeded and cut into ½-inch dice
- ▲ ½ English (seedless) cucumber, cut into ½-inch dice
- ▲ ½ cup roasted red pepper (not packed in oil), cut into ½-inch dice
- ▲ 1 small sweet onion, cut into ½-inch dice
- ½ cup (½-inch) diced low-sodium Swiss cheese

1 To make dressing, whisk together mayonnaise, yogurt, relish, ketchup, Worcestershire sauce, celery seeds, and black pepper in serving bowl until blended.

2 Line salad bowl with lettuce.

3 Combine remaining ingredients in large bowl and toss until mixed. Spoon over lettuce. Serve dressing alongside.

PER SERVING (*about 1 cup salad and ¼ cup dressing*): 149 Cal, 5 g Total Fat, 2 g Sat Fat, 0 g Trans Fat, 13 mg Chol, 585 mg Sod, 21 g Carb, 11 g Sugar, 3 g Fib, 7 g Prot, 191 mg Calc.

stay on track

Want to add a bit of summer and fiber to this kitchen sink–type salad? Add 1½ cups of fresh corn kernels (about 2 small ears of corn) to the chickpea mixture. This will increase the per-serving *PointsPlus* value by *1*.

CHARRED BEETS WITH PISTACHIOS AND GORGONZOLA

charred beets with pistachios and gorgonzola

SERVES 4

PER SERVING

- ▲ **4 small beets, scrubbed and stem ends trimmed to 1-inch**
- **¼ cup + 1 tablespoon red-wine vinegar**
- **4 fresh thyme sprigs + ½ teaspoon thyme leaves**
- **2 bay leaves**
- **½ teaspoon salt**
- **½ teaspoon black pepper**
- **1 tablespoon minced shallot**
- **2 teaspoons extra-virgin olive oil**
- **1 teaspoon water**
- ▲ **5 cups lightly packed mesclun or other baby greens**
- **2 tablespoons chopped pistachios**
- **2 tablespoons crumbled Gorgonzola cheese**

1 Put beets in medium saucepan and add ¼ cup of vinegar, the thyme sprigs, bay leaves, ¼ teaspoon of salt, and ¼ teaspoon of pepper. Add enough cold water to cover beets by about 1 inch and bring to boil. Reduce heat and simmer until beets are fork-tender, 35–40 minutes. Drain beets and let cool slightly. Discard thyme sprigs and bay leaves.

2 Meanwhile, to make dressing, whisk together shallot, oil, remaining 1 tablespoon vinegar, the water, thyme leaves, and remaining ¼ teaspoon salt and ¼ teaspoon pepper in large bowl.

3 Trim stem and root ends from beets. Place beets, one at a time, between two layers of parchment or wax paper; gently press with your hand to partially flatten, making sure beet stays intact (the edges will split).

4 Heat large cast-iron skillet over medium-high heat until very hot. Lightly spray beets with olive oil nonstick spray. Add beets to skillet and cook, carefully turning once with metal spatula, until skins are nicely charred, about 5 minutes. Transfer beets to plate.

5 Add mesclun to dressing and toss until coated evenly. Divide greens among 4 plates. Top each with 1 beet and sprinkle evenly with pistachios and Gorgonzola.

PER SERVING (*1 salad*): 105 cal, 6 g Fat, 2 g Sat Fat, 0 g Trans Fat, 5 mg Chol, 433 mg Sod, 11 g Carb, 6 g Sugar, 4 g Fib, 4 g Prot, 43 mg Calc.

for your info

Boiling the whole beets, then charring them in the skillet makes the beet skins delicious and tender.

blood orange and spinach salad with toasted walnuts

SERVES 6

▲ 1 shallot, minced

▲ 3 blood oranges or navel oranges, peeled and sectioned, 2 tablespoons juice reserved

1½ tablespoons cider vinegar

1½ teaspoons extra-virgin olive oil

1 teaspoon Dijon mustard

½ teaspoon salt

¼ teaspoon black pepper

▲ 1 (5-ounce) container baby spinach

⅓ cup cherry-flavored dried cranberries

¼ cup + 2 tablespoons crumbled reduced-fat blue cheese

¼ cup walnuts, toasted and chopped

1 To make dressing, whisk together shallot, reserved orange juice, the vinegar, oil, mustard, salt, and pepper in small bowl until blended.

2 Combine spinach, orange segments, and dried cranberries in large bowl. Drizzle dressing over salad and toss until coated evenly. Divide salad among 6 plates; sprinkle evenly with blue cheese and walnuts.

PER SERVING (1⅔ cups): 137 Cal, 6 g Total Fat, 2 g Sat Fat, 0 g Trans Fat, 6 mg Chol, 328 mg Sod, 18 g Carb, 11 g Sugar, 3 g Fib, 5 g Prot, 113 mg Calc.

now try this

Blood oranges, also called Moros, are mostly available from January through April. They come small to medium and have thin skins and very few seeds, if any. The color of their flesh ranges from bright red to deep maroon, and they have an intense orange flavor with strong notes of fresh raspberries. Their magnificent color comes from a high concentration of anthocyanins, a powerful antioxidant also found in deeply colored berries.

grilled bartlett pear salad with pomegranate vinaigrette

SERVES 4

PER SERVING

- ▲ **2 ripe Bartlett pears, halved, cored, and each cut into 6 wedges**
- **1 tablespoon red-wine vinegar**
- **1 tablespoon pomegranate juice**
- **1 tablespoon honey**
- **2 teaspoons extra-virgin olive oil**
- **1 teaspoon Dijon mustard**
- **¼ teaspoon salt**
- **⅛ teaspoon black pepper**
- ▲ **5 cups lightly packed mesclun**
- **3 tablespoons sliced almonds, toasted**

1 Spray grill rack with nonstick spray. Preheat grill to medium-high or prepare medium-high fire.

2 Lightly spray pears with olive oil nonstick spray. Place, cut side down, on grill rack and grill until tender and well marked, about 2 minutes per cut side. Transfer pears to plate.

3 To make dressing, whisk together vinegar, pomegranate juice, honey, oil, mustard, salt, and pepper in small bowl.

4 Put mesclun in large bowl and drizzle with dressing; toss until coated evenly. Divide mesclun among 4 plates; top each with 3 pear wedges and sprinkle evenly with almonds.

PER SERVING (*about 1½ cups*): 129 Cal, 5 g Fat, 1 g Sat Fat, 0 g Trans Fat, 0 mg Chol, 202 mg Sod, 23 g Carb, 15 g Sugar, 5 g Fib, 2 g Prot, 21 mg Calc.

watercress salad with fuyu persimmons and sherry vinaigrette

SERVES 4 • 20 MINUTES

5
PointsPlus©
value

PER SERVING

▲ **2 scallions, thinly sliced**

2 teaspoons hazelnut or olive oil

2 teaspoons sherry vinegar

1 teaspoon water

1 teaspoon dark agave nectar (see tip page 109) or honey

¼ teaspoon salt

⅛ teaspoon black pepper

▲ **1 bunch watercress, trimmed (about 6 cups lightly packed sprigs)**

▲ **4 small firm fuyu persimmons, cut into thin wedges**

4 thin slices speck or prosciutto (about ½ ounce each), trimmed

▲ **2 tablespoons crumbled fat-free feta cheese**

1 To make dressing, whisk together scallions, oil, vinegar, water, agave nectar, salt, and pepper in large bowl.

2 Add watercress and persimmons to dressing; toss until coated evenly. Ruffle slices of speck on platter; place watercress salad alongside and sprinkle evenly with feta.

PER SERVING (1¼ *cups salad and 1 slice speck*): 186 cal, 4 g Fat, 1 g Sat Fat, 0 g Trans Fat, 12 mg Chol, 614 mg Sod, 33 g Carb, 21 g Sugar, 7 g Fib, 8 g Prot, 110 mg Calc.

now try this

Speck, smoked prosciutto, comes from the Alto Adige region of Italy, where the food is heavily influenced by its German neighbor. To make speck, prosciutto is first cured, then slowly smoked over juniper or pine for several hours a day for about 3 months. This slow smoking ensures that the inner layers of the prosciutto are fully permeated with smoke.

WATERCRESS SALAD WITH FUYU
PERSIMMONS AND SHERRY VINAIGRETTE

grilled radicchio with dried currants and toasted pine nuts

SERVES 4 • 20 MINUTES

2
PointsPlus©
value®

PER SERVING

2 tablespoons packed dark brown sugar

1 tablespoon good-quality balsamic vinegar

¼ teaspoon salt

⅛ teaspoon black pepper

▲ 1 small head radicchio (about 6 ounces), quartered

▲ 4 cups lightly packed baby arugula or mesclun

2 tablespoons dried currants

1 tablespoon pine nuts, toasted and chopped

2 teaspoons extra-virgin olive oil

1 Combine brown sugar and vinegar in small saucepan and set over low heat. Cook, stirring constantly, until sugar is dissolved. Bring to boil, stirring constantly. Remove saucepan from heat and stir in salt and pepper. Keep warm.

2 Heat ridged grill pan over medium-high heat until hot. Lightly spray radicchio with olive oil nonstick spray. Add radicchio to pan, cut side down, and grill, turning, until edges are charred and radicchio is wilted, about 8 minutes.

3 Divide arugula among 4 plates. Place 1 radicchio wedge on each plate; drizzle evenly with balsamic glaze and sprinkle evenly with currants and pine nuts. Drizzle evenly with oil.

PER SERVING (*1 salad*): 82 cal, 4 g Fat, 0 g Sat Fat, 0 g Trans Fat, 0 mg Chol, 154 mg Sod, 12 g Carb, 11 g Sugar, 1 g Fib, 1 g Prot, 45 mg Calc.

For more vegetable goodness, halve and grill two heads of Belgian endive to add to this special salad.

lentil, bean, and arugula salad with curry dressing

SERVES 4

▲ ½ cup lentils, rinsed and picked over

2 cups water

1 tablespoon cider vinegar

1 tablespoon olive oil

1½ teaspoons curry powder

¼ teaspoon salt

▲ 4 cups lightly packed mesclun

▲ 1 cup canned small white beans, rinsed and drained

▲ 1 tomato, diced

▲ 1 small yellow bell pepper, chopped

▲ ½ cup thinly sliced red onion

▲ 2 mini cucumbers, quartered lengthwise and sliced

1 Combine lentils and water in medium saucepan; bring to boil. Reduce heat and simmer, covered, until lentils are tender, about 20 minutes; drain and let cool.

2 Meanwhile, to make dressing, whisk together vinegar, oil, curry powder, and salt in serving bowl. Add lentils, mesclun, beans, tomato, pepper, onion, and cucumbers; toss until coated evenly.

PER SERVING (*1 cup*): 191 Cal, 5 g Total Fat, 1 g Sat Fat, 0 g Trans Fat, 0 mg Chol, 396 mg Sod, 34 g Carb, 6 g Sugar, 10 g Fib, 11 g Prot, 74 mg Calc.

chapter 3

between the bread

sandwiches, pizzas, and breads

spicy pepper and onion steak sandwiches

SERVES 4

½ teaspoon olive oil

▲ 3 red bell peppers, thinly sliced

▲ 1 large red onion, thinly sliced

3 large garlic cloves, minced

1 teaspoon dried oregano

¼ teaspoon salt

¼ teaspoon black pepper

1 teaspoon hot pepper sauce or to taste

▲ 4 (¼-pound) lean beef cube steaks, trimmed

1 (8-ounce) whole grain baguette, split and lightly toasted

1 Coat large nonstick skillet with oil and set over medium heat. Add bell peppers and cook, stirring frequently, until crisp-tender, about 5 minutes. Add onion, garlic, oregano, salt, and black pepper; cook until vegetables are softened, about 5 minutes longer. Transfer vegetable mixture to medium bowl. Add pepper sauce and toss; keep warm.

2 Spray steaks on both sides with nonstick spray. Wipe out skillet and set over medium heat. Add steaks and cook until cooked through, about 3 minutes per side.

3 Cut bread into 4 equal pieces. Place 1 steak on bottom of each piece of bread; top evenly with bell pepper mixture. Cover with tops of bread.

PER SERVING (1 sandwich): 416 Cal, 10 g Total Fat, 3 g Sat Fat, 0 g Trans Fat, 75 mg Chol, 499 mg Sod, 39 g Carb, 10 g Sugar, 7 g Fib, 42 g Prot, 92 mg Calc.

stay on track

These sandwiches are a little higher in *PointsPlus* value than some, but with plenty of protein and fiber they're bound to keep you satisfied all afternoon. If you like, serve them with a side of broccoli slaw dressed with red-wine vinegar.

turkey pita sandwiches with fresh mint–yogurt sauce

SERVES 4 • 20 MINUTES

PER SERVING

- ▲ ¾ cup plain fat-free Greek yogurt
- ▲ ⅓ cup finely diced cucumber
- 3 tablespoons chopped fresh mint
- 1 garlic clove, minced
- ½ teaspoon red-wine vinegar
- ⅛ teaspoon black pepper
- Few drops hot pepper sauce
- 2 (6½-inch) whole wheat pita breads
- ▲ 4 small butter or green leaf lettuce leaves
- ▲ 1½ cups shredded cooked skinless turkey breast
- ▲ 1 tomato, cut into 8 wedges
- ▲ ½ small red onion, thinly sliced

1 To make sauce, stir together yogurt, cucumber, mint, garlic, vinegar, black pepper, and pepper sauce in small bowl.

2 Cut each pita in half. Line each pita half with 1 lettuce leaf and fill evenly with turkey, tomato, and onion. Top each with one-fourth of sauce.

PER SERVING (½ sandwich): 239 Cal, 2 g Total Fat, 1 g Sat Fat, 0 g Trans Fat, 71 mg Chol, 237 mg Sod, 23 g Carb, 4 g Sugar, 4 g Fib, 34 g Prot, 64 mg Calc.

salmon, kalamata olive, and red onion sandwiches

SERVES 4 • 20 MINUTES

PER SERVING

- ▲ 1 (7½-ounce) can no-salt-added water-packed salmon, drained and flaked
- ▲ ½ cup peeled, seeded, and chopped cucumber
- ▲ ¼ cup chopped red onion
-   8 pitted Kalamata olives, chopped
- ▲ 3 tablespoons plain fat-free yogurt
-   2 tablespoons chopped fresh mint
-   Finely grated zest and juice of ½ lime
-   Few drops hot pepper sauce
-   1 (5-ounce) length whole wheat bread, split
- ▲ 4 red leaf lettuce leaves
- ▲ 8 thick slices tomato

1 Stir together salmon, cucumber, onion, olives, yogurt, mint, lime zest and juice, and pepper sauce in medium bowl.

2 Line bottom of bread with lettuce and tomato. Spoon salmon mixture on top and cover with top of bread. Cut into 4 sandwiches.

PER SERVING (*1 sandwich*): 221 Cal, 7 g Total Fat, 1 g Sat Fat, 0 g Trans Fat, 24 mg Chol, 371 mg Sod, 24 g Carb, 4 g Sugar, 3 g Fib, 16 g Prot, 168 mg Calc.

stay on track

Enjoy a few grapes or a delicious piece of stone fruit, such as a peach, nectarine, apricot, or plum, for dessert.

open-face poached egg, asparagus, and prosciutto sandwiches

SERVES 2

7
PointsPlus©
value®
PER SERVING

▲ **2 tablespoons plain fat-free Greek yogurt**

1½ tablespoons reduced-fat mayonnaise

2 teaspoons chopped fresh tarragon + 2 tarragon sprigs for garnish

1 teaspoon finely grated orange zest

1 tablespoon orange juice

¼ teaspoon Aleppo pepper or pinch cayenne

4 cups + 1 tablespoon water

1 teaspoon cider vinegar

▲ **2 large eggs**

▲ **14 thin asparagus spears, trimmed**

2 (1-ounce) slices whole grain country-style bread, toasted

4 thin slices prosciutto (about ½ ounce each)

1 To make sauce, whisk together yogurt, mayonnaise, chopped tarragon, orange zest and juice, and Aleppo pepper in small bowl until blended. Set aside.

2 To poach eggs, combine 4 cups of water and the vinegar in medium nonstick skillet and bring to boil. Reduce heat to bare simmer. Break 1 egg into cup. Holding cup close to water, slide egg into water. Repeat with remaining egg. Cook until whites are firm but yolks are still soft, about 5 minutes. With slotted spoon, transfer eggs, one at a time, to paper towel–lined plate to drain. Keep warm.

3 Meanwhile, put asparagus and remaining 1 tablespoon water in glass pie plate. Cover loosely with wax paper and microwave on High until crisp-tender, 2–3 minutes.

4 To serve, place 1 slice of toast on each of 2 plates; top each with 7 asparagus spears. Place poached egg on top of asparagus and ruffle 2 slices of prosciutto alongside. Spoon 2 tablespoons of sauce over each egg and garnish with tarragon sprig.

PER SERVING (*1 sandwich*): 262 Cal, 10 g Total Fat, 3 g Sat Fat, 0 g Trans Fat, 237 mg Chol, 1046 mg Sod, 22 g Carb, 6 g Sugar, 5 g Fib, 22 g Prot, 92 mg Calc.

now try this

Aleppo pepper is named after the city of Aleppo, which is located along the Silk Road in northern Syria. It is used extensively in Middle Eastern and Mediterranean cooking. The pepper pods are allowed to ripen to a deep red and are then partially dried before being seeded and crushed or coarsely ground. Aleppo pepper contains only a moderate amount of heat.

OPEN-FACE POACHED EGG, ASPARAGUS, AND PROSCIUTTO SANDWICHES

tuna and fennel melts on toasted olive ciabatta

SERVES 2

6 PointsPlus value PER SERVING

▲ 1 (5-ounce) can no-salt-added light tuna packed in water, drained

▲ ½ cup diced fresh fennel + 1 tablespoon chopped fronds

▲ 3 tablespoons chopped red onion

▲ 3 tablespoons coarsely chopped roasted red pepper (not packed in oil)

2 tablespoons reduced-fat mayonnaise

1 teaspoon finely grated lemon zest

1 teaspoon lemon juice

½ teaspoon tiny (nonpareil) capers, drained and rinsed

¼ teaspoon black pepper

2 (2-ounce) slices olive or rosemary ciabatta bread, toasted

¼ cup coarsely shredded Gruyère (see tip page 21) or Swiss cheese

1 Flake tuna into medium bowl. Add fennel and fronds, onion, roasted pepper, mayonnaise, lemon zest and juice, capers, and black pepper; mix until blended but still chunky.

2 Preheat broiler.

3 Mound tuna mixture over slices of toast, dividing evenly. Sprinkle each sandwich with 2 tablespoons Gruyère. Place sandwiches on broiler rack and broil 5 inches from heat until tuna is heated through and cheese is melted and bubbly, about 4 minutes.

PER SERVING (*1 sandwich*): 264 Cal, 8 g Total Fat, 3 g Sat Fat, 0 g Trans Fat, 36 mg Chol, 485 mg Sod, 22 g Carb, 3 g Sugar, 3 g Fib, 25 g Prot, 173 mg Calc.

now try this

Ciabatta, also known as slipper bread, is a flat, elongated loaf with an open texture and a moist crumb. It has a crust that is firm but not too hard, making it ideal for sandwiches. There are many variations, including plain, whole wheat, raisin, and olive.

maple-bacon tempeh blts with lemon mayo

SERVES 2 • 20 MINUTES

PER SERVING

½ teaspoon olive oil

6 slices smoky maple-bacon tempeh

3 tablespoons fat-free mayonnaise

1 teaspoon finely grated lemon zest

▲ 4 slices reduced-calorie whole grain bread, toasted

▲ 1 large tomato, preferably heirloom, thickly sliced

¼ Hass avocado, peeled and thinly sliced

8 fresh basil leaves

▲ 2 Boston or butter lettuce leaves

1 Coat medium cast-iron or other heavy skillet with oil and set over medium-high heat. Add tempeh and cook until nicely browned, about 2 minutes per side. Transfer to plate; keep warm.

2 Stir together mayonnaise and lemon zest in cup.

3 Spread lemon mayonnaise evenly on 2 slices of toast. Top evenly with tomato, avocado, basil, tempeh, and lettuce. Cover sandwiches with remaining 2 slices of toast.

PER SERVING (1 sandwich): 237 Cal, 8 g Total Fat, 1 g Sat Fat, 0 g Trans Fat, 2 mg Chol, 666 mg Sod, 33 g Carb, 8 g Sugar, 11 g Fib, 13 g Prot, 150 mg Calc.

spinach, roasted tomato, and smoked gouda paninis

SERVES 2

- 3 plum tomatoes, cut lengthwise into ½-inch slices
- 1 garlic clove, peeled
- ½ teaspoon dried oregano
- ⅛ teaspoon red pepper flakes
- 4 slices reduced-calorie bread
- 2 teaspoons whole grain mustard, such as Maille
- ⅔ cup lightly packed baby spinach
- ⅓ cup coarsely shredded smoked Gouda or other smoked cheese

1 Preheat oven to 400°F. Lightly spray 9-inch pie plate with olive oil nonstick spray.

2 Arrange tomatoes in single layer in prepared pie plate. With knife, mince garlic, then add oregano, and pepper flakes and chop until blended well. Spread garlic mixture evenly over tomatoes. Bake until tomatoes are very tender and dry-looking, about 30 minutes. Cover loosely with sheet of wax paper and set aside.

3 Preheat panini maker to high.

4 Meanwhile, spray one side of each slice of bread with nonstick spray. Place, sprayed side down, on work surface. Spread mustard over 2 slices of bread. Layer evenly with spinach and tomatoes; sprinkle with Gouda. Cover sandwiches with remaining slices of bread, sprayed side facing up.

5 Place sandwiches in panini maker. Close lid and cook until bread is well marked and crisp and cheese is melted, about 4 minutes.

PER SERVING (1 sandwich): 171 Cal, 6 g Total Fat, 3 g Sat Fat, 0 g Trans Fat, 21 mg Chol, 412 mg Sod, 26 g Carb, 6 g Sugar, 8 g Fib, 10 g Prot, 194 mg Calc.

mushroom, baby spinach, and jarlsberg quesadillas

SERVES 8

4 PointsPlus value

PER SERVING

▲ 8 ounces cremini mushrooms, sliced

▲ 1 (5-ounce) container baby spinach

8 (7-inch) fat-free whole wheat tortillas

1 cup coarsely shredded part-skim Jarlsberg cheese

4 ounces reduced-fat soft goat cheese, crumbled

▲ 2 scallions, thinly sliced

▲ 2 tablespoons sliced pickled jalapeño peppers, drained and finely chopped

1 Put mushrooms in large nonstick skillet and spray with olive oil nonstick spray. Set over medium heat and cook, stirring, until mushrooms are golden and softened, about 6 minutes. Add spinach and cook, stirring, until wilted, about 3 minutes longer. Transfer vegetable mixture to plate and let cool slightly.

2 Lay 4 tortillas on work surface. Layer each with one-fourth of mushroom-spinach mixture, Jarlsberg, goat cheese, scallions, and jalapeños. Top with remaining 4 tortillas, lightly pressing down.

3 Wipe skillet clean and set over medium heat. Spray top of 1 quesadilla with nonstick spray; place, sprayed side down, in skillet and cook until tortilla is crisp and cheese begins to melt, about 2 minutes. Spray tortilla; turn quesadilla over and cook until browned in spots and crispy, about 2 minutes longer. Transfer to cutting board and cover loosely with foil to keep warm. Repeat with remaining 3 quesadillas. Cut each quesadilla into 4 wedges, making total of 16 wedges.

PER SERVING (*2 wedges*): 153 Cal, 5 g Total Fat, 2 g Sat Fat, 0 g Trans Fat, 9 mg Chol, 609 mg Sod, 17 g Carb, 2 g Sugar, 8 g Fib, 16 g Prot, 220 mg Calc.

stay on track

These vegetable-cheese quesadillas pack a big flavor punch for a relatively low *PointsPlus* value. You can add some additional color, fiber, and flavor by sprinkling chopped red bell pepper onto each quesadilla along with the other ingredients in step 2 without changing the *PointsPlus* value.

plum tomato–basil pizza margherita

SERVES 6

▲ **4 large plum tomatoes, thinly sliced**

1 tablespoon extra-virgin olive oil

¾ teaspoon dried oregano

⅛ teaspoon black pepper

⅛ teaspoon red pepper flakes

1 (10½-ounce) prebaked multigrain pizza crust

6 ounces part-skim mozzarella cheese, thinly sliced

¼ cup lightly packed fresh basil leaves, torn if large

1 Preheat oven to 450°F. Spray baking sheet with nonstick spray.

2 Toss together tomatoes, 1 teaspoon of oil, the oregano, black pepper, and pepper flakes in medium bowl; let stand 5 minutes.

3 Place crust on prepared baking sheet. Spread tomatoes evenly over crust; top evenly with mozzarella. Bake until cheese is melted, about 8 minutes. Sprinkle with basil; drizzle with remaining 2 teaspoons oil and cut into 6 wedges.

PER SERVING (*1 wedge*): 227 Cal, 9 g Total Fat, 4 g Sat Fat, 0 g Trans Fat, 15 mg Chol, 361 mg Sod, 24 g Carb, 1 g Sugar, 3 g Fib, 11 g Prot, 231 mg Calc.

for your info

Fairly new to the market are moist, flavorful prebaked pizza crusts that are chock full of whole grains. You can find versions containing grains and seeds, such as wheat bran, whole wheat flour, whole triticale flour, rye flour, flax seeds, oat flakes, and cracked wheat.

fresh fig, gorgonzola, and prosciutto pizza

SERVES 8

1 (10-ounce) prebaked thin whole wheat pizza crust

4 ounces gorgonzola cheese, crumbled

8 thin slices prosciutto (½-ounce each), halved crosswise

▲ 2 cups lightly packed baby arugula

▲ 6 fresh figs, torn into rough chunks

1 tablespoon fig or regular balsamic vinegar

1 Preheat oven to 450°F.

2 Place pizza crust on baking sheet and sprinkle with gorgonzola. Bake until crust is very crisp on bottom, about 12 minutes. Immediately top with prosciutto, arugula, and figs; drizzle with vinegar. Cut into 8 wedges and serve.

PER SERVING (*1 wedge*): 178 Cal, 7 g Total Fat, 3 g Sat Fat, 0 g Trans Fat, 24 mg Chol, 704 mg Sod, 21 g Carb, 4 g Sugar, 3 g Fib, 10 g Prot, 95 mg Calc.

no-knead tomato-oregano pizza

SERVES 8

- 1¼ cups white whole wheat flour
- ½ cup all-purpose flour
- 1⅛ teaspoons active dry yeast (half of ¼-ounce envelope)
- ¼ teaspoon sugar
- ¼ teaspoon salt
- ¾ cup water
- ▲ 1 (14½-ounce) can diced tomatoes in juice, drained
- 1 tablespoon + 2 teaspoons extra-virgin olive oil
- 2 garlic cloves, minced
- ¾ teaspoon dried oregano
- ¼ teaspoon red pepper flakes
- ▲ 1 cup thinly sliced red or white onion

1 To make dough, whisk together white whole wheat flour, all-purpose flour, yeast, sugar, and salt in large bowl. Add water and stir until dough forms. If needed, stir in 1 to 2 tablespoons water. Cover and let stand at room temperature (80–85°F) about 2 hours. (It won't rise much.)

2 To make tomato sauce, puree tomatoes in food processor.

3 Heat 2 teaspoons of oil in medium nonstick skillet over medium heat. Add garlic, ½ teaspoon of oregano, and the pepper flakes; cook, stirring, until garlic turns golden. Add tomatoes and simmer until consistency of tomato puree, about 3 minutes. Remove skillet from heat.

4 Meanwhile, place oven rack in middle of oven and preheat to 500°F. Coat 10½ x 15½-inch jelly-roll pan with remaining 1 tablespoon oil.

5 Place dough in center of pan and push it out with your fingertips to pan edges. (If dough springs back, let rest 5 minutes.) Spread sauce over dough. Sprinkle with onion and remaining ¼ teaspoon oregano.

6 Bake until crust is golden and puffed along edges and browned on bottom, 13–15 minutes. Transfer to cutting board. With scissors or pizza cutter, cut lengthwise in half, then crosswise in quarters.

PER SERVING (*1 piece*): 146 Cal, 4 g Total Fat, 1 g Sat Fat, 0 g Trans Fat, 0 mg Chol, 215 mg Sod, 25 g Carb, 2 g Sugar, 3 g Fib, 4 g Prot, 34 mg Calc.

CLOCKWISE FROM TOP LEFT:
FLAKY PHYLLO-CRUSTED PIZZA
WITH CHERRY TOMATOES, p.97,
YUKON GOLD POTATO PIZZA WITH
TRUFFLE OIL, p.96, NO-KNEAD
TOMATO-OREGANO PIZZA

yukon gold potato pizza with truffle oil

SERVES 6

▲ **2 (8-ounce) Yukon Gold potatoes, peeled**

4 cups water

½ teaspoon salt

1 pound refrigerated whole wheat pizza dough, at room temperature

▲ **½ cup chopped red onion**

1 tablespoon chopped fresh rosemary

2 teaspoons extra-virgin olive oil

¼ teaspoon black pepper

▲ **2 cups thinly sliced cremini mushrooms**

1½ teaspoons white truffle oil

1 With vegetable slicer or sharp knife, cut potatoes into $\frac{1}{16}$-inch slices. Combine water and salt in large bowl, stirring until salt is dissolved. Add potatoes and let stand 15 minutes. Drain. Pat potatoes dry with double layer of paper towels. Rinse and dry bowl; return potatoes to bowl.

2 Meanwhile, preheat oven to 475°F.

3 On lightly floured work surface with lightly floured rolling pin, roll dough into 12-inch round; transfer to 14½-inch pizza pan and stretch dough to fit pan.

4 Add onion, rosemary, olive oil, and pepper to potatoes. Toss potatoes until coated evenly. Arrange potatoes in concentric circles or in other pattern over dough, overlapping slices. Arrange mushrooms in middle of pizza, leaving potatoes exposed around edge.

5 Bake until potatoes are tender and golden and crust is browned along edge, about 20 minutes. Drizzle evenly with truffle oil and cut into 6 wedges.

PER SERVING (*1 wedge*): 269 Cal, 5 g Total Fat, 0 g Sat Fat, 0 g Trans Fat, 0 mg Chol, 526 mg Sod, 48 g Carb, 2 g Sugar, 6 g Fib, 7 g Prot, 46 mg Calc.

flaky phyllo-crusted pizza with cherry tomatoes and crumbled feta

SERVES 6

4
PointsPlus®
value

PER SERVING

▲ **3 cups red and yellow cherry and/ or grape tomatoes**

1 tablespoon extra-virgin olive oil

1 large garlic clove, minced

½ teaspoon dried Italian seasoning

¼ teaspoon salt

⅛ teaspoon black pepper

6 (12 x 16-inch) sheets phyllo dough, thawed if frozen

1¼ cups coarsely shredded part-skim mozzarella cheese

▲ **⅓ cup crumbled fat-free tomato-basil feta cheese**

¼ cup thinly sliced fresh basil

2 tablespoons chopped fresh oregano

1 Preheat oven to 400°F. Lightly spray 9-inch pie plate and rimmed baking sheet with olive oil nonstick spray.

2 Put tomatoes in prepared pie plate. Mix together oil, garlic, Italian seasoning, salt, and pepper in cup. Add 1½ teaspoons of garlic-oil mixture to tomatoes, tossing to coat. Roast until tomatoes start to collapse, about 15 minutes. Let cool.

3 Reduce oven temperature to 375°F.

4 Put 1 sheet of phyllo on prepared baking sheet; spray with nonstick spray. Stack 4 more sheets of phyllo, lightly spraying each. Place remaining sheet of phyllo on top. With rubber spatula, gently and evenly spread remaining garlic-oil over phyllo. Mix together mozzarella and feta in small bowl; sprinkle evenly over phyllo, leaving ¼-inch border. Top evenly with tomatoes and any juice.

5 Bake until phyllo is crisp and browned along edges and mozzarella is melted, about 15 minutes. Transfer to wire rack and let stand 5 minutes. Sprinkle with basil and oregano. Cut pizza lengthwise in half then crosswise into thirds.

PER SERVING (*1 piece*): 171 Cal, 8 g Total Fat, 4 g Sat Fat, 0 g Trans Fat, 13 mg Chol, 373 mg Sod, 14 g Carb, 2 g Sugar, 1 g Fib, 10 g Prot, 211 mg Calc.

stay on track

Get more satisfaction and a healthy dose of vitamins and minerals by enjoying this pizza along with a dark leafy green salad of romaine, arugula, watercress, and escarole dressed with lemon juice.

escarole-stuffed pizza with pepperoni and fontina

SERVES 8

1 pound refrigerated whole wheat pizza dough

1 tablespoon extra-virgin olive oil

6 garlic cloves, thinly sliced

▲ 1 large onion, chopped

¼–½ teaspoon red pepper flakes

12 slices turkey pepperoni, coarsely chopped

▲ 12 cups lightly packed thinly sliced escarole (about 1 head)

▲ 6 cups lightly packed thinly sliced Swiss chard leaves (about 1 bunch)

½ teaspoon black pepper

1 cup coarsely shredded fontina cheese

1 Preheat oven to 450°F. Lightly spray 2 x 9-inch round cake pan or 9-inch springform pan with olive oil nonstick spray.

2 Cut off one-third of dough (keep remaining dough covered with plastic wrap). On lightly floured work surface with floured rolling pin, roll dough into 9-inch round. Place in prepared pan and stretch dough until it covers bottom of pan. Prick all over with fork and lightly spray with nonstick spray. Bake until light golden, 10–12 minutes. Transfer to wire rack and let cool.

3 Meanwhile, heat oil in Dutch oven over medium heat. Add garlic and cook, stirring often, until golden, about 2 minutes. Stir in onion and pepper flakes; cook, stirring, until onion is softened, about 5 minutes. Add pepperoni and cook, stirring, until heated through, about 2 minutes longer.

4 Add escarole and chard, in batches, to pot and cook, stirring, until wilted, about 5 minutes. Sprinkle with black pepper. Cook, stirring, until greens are very tender and any liquid is evaporated, about 12 minutes. Transfer vegetables to large bowl and let cool slightly.

5 Spread cooled greens over crust, leaving ¼-inch border. Sprinkle evenly with fontina. On lightly floured work surface with floured rolling pin, roll remaining dough into 10-inch round. Place dough over filling, tucking edge under bottom crust to completely enclose filling, pressing to seal. Lightly spray dough with nonstick spray.

6 Bake until crust is browned and shrinks away from side of pan, about 20 minutes. Invert pizza onto wire rack, then turn right side up. Let cool 10 to 15 minutes before cutting into 8 wedges.

PER SERVING (1 wedge): 247 Cal, 9 g Total Fat, 3 g Sat Fat, 0 g Trans Fat, 26 mg Chol, 582 mg Sod, 31 g Carb, 2 g Sugar, 6 g Fib, 12 g Prot, 158 mg Calc.

orange and cardamom–scented irish soda bread

SERVES 12

1 cup all-purpose flour

1 cup white whole wheat flour

3 tablespoons sugar

1 teaspoon baking powder

¾ teaspoon salt

½ teaspoon ground cardamom

½ teaspoon baking soda

2 tablespoons cold unsalted butter, cut into pieces

½ cup dark raisins, chopped

2–3 teaspoons caraway seeds

1 cup low-fat buttermilk

Finely grated zest of ½ large orange

▲ 1 large egg, beaten, for egg wash

1 Preheat oven to 350°F. Spray baking sheet with nonstick spray and lightly sprinkle with flour.

2 Whisk together all-purpose flour, white whole wheat flour, sugar, baking powder, salt, cardamom, and baking soda in large bowl. With pastry blender or two knives used scissor-fashion, cut in butter until mixture is crumbly. Stir in raisins and caraway seeds. Whisk together buttermilk and orange zest in small bowl; add to flour mixture, stirring with wooden spoon just until flour mixture is moistened.

3 Knead flour mixture in bowl 5 or 6 times, just until dough forms. Shape into 6-inch round loaf and transfer to prepared baking sheet.

4 Brush loaf with egg wash. With serrated knife, cut ½-inch-deep X in top of loaf. Bake until golden brown and toothpick inserted into center comes out clean, about 45 minutes. Serve warm or let cool completely on wire rack. Cut into 12 wedges.

PER SERVING (*1 wedge*): 142 Cal, 3 g Total Fat, 1 g Sat Fat, 0 g Trans Fat, 24 mg Chol, 273 mg Sod, 25 g Carb, 8 g Sugar, 2 g Fib, 4 g Prot, 44 mg Calc.

for your info

The Society for the Preservation of Irish Soda Bread, www.sodabread.info, is dedicated to promoting Irish soda bread as it was prepared by generations past in Ireland. A traditional soda bread doesn't have raisins, sugar, orange zest, eggs, shortening, or any of the other tasty ingredients that today's Irish-American versions often contain. An authentic soda bread is made with wheat flour, salt, baking soda, water, and sour milk.

FRESH ROSEMARY AND
OLIVE-STUDDED BREAD

fresh rosemary and olive-studded bread

SERVES 12

4 PointsPlus value

PER SERVING

1¼ cups warm water (105–115°F)

1 tablespoon sugar

1 envelope active dry yeast

2 tablespoons extra-virgin olive oil

3¼ cups white whole wheat flour

2 tablespoons chopped fresh rosemary

1 teaspoon salt

20 pitted brine-cured green and/or black olives, halved

▲ 1 large egg yolk beaten with 1 tablespoon water, for egg wash

Coarsely ground black pepper

1 Combine water and sugar in glass measure. Sprinkle in yeast and let stand until foamy, about 5 minutes; stir in oil.

2 Combine 3 cups of flour, the rosemary, and salt in large bowl. Add yeast mixture; with wooden spoon, stir until dough forms. Add olives and knead 5 or 6 times or until incorporated. Turn dough onto lightly floured work surface. Knead until smooth and elastic, about 10 minutes, adding enough of remaining ¼ cup flour to keep dough from sticking.

3 Spray clean large bowl with nonstick spray; place dough in bowl and turn to coat. Cover bowl with plastic wrap and let dough rise in warm place (80–85°F) until doubled in size, about 1½ hours.

4 Lightly flour large baking sheet. Punch down dough. Turn onto floured surface and knead 10 times. Shape into 6-inch round and transfer to baking sheet. Cover and let rise in warm place until doubled, about 30 minutes.

5 Meanwhile, preheat oven to 400°F. Brush egg wash over bread and sprinkle with pepper. With sharp knife, cut several ½-inch-deep slashes in loaf. Bake until golden brown and loaf sounds hollow when tapped, 40–45 minutes. Transfer bread to wire rack and let cool completely. Cut into 12 slices.

PER SERVING (*1 slice*): 166 Cal, 4 g Total Fat, 1 g Sat Fat, 0 g Trans Fat, 17 mg Chol, 266 mg Sod, 27 g Carb, 1 g Sugar, 5 g Fib, 5 g Prot, 7 mg Calc.

stay on track

How about a tasty and satisfying low *PointsPlus* value lunch? Have a mixed salad and a bowl of warming bouillion—any kind—along with a slice of this bread topped with a 1-ounce slice of fat-free sharp Cheddar cheese—melted if you like. This will increase the per-serving *PointsPlus* value by *1*.

crescent rolls with nigella seeds

MAKES 12

1 cup warm water (105–115°F)

1½ tablespoons light agave nectar (see tip page 109) or 1 tablespoon honey

1½ cups all-purpose flour

1 cup white whole wheat flour

1 envelope quick-rise yeast

1¼ teaspoons salt

▲ 1 large egg, beaten, for egg wash

2–3 teaspoons nigella seeds or black sesame seeds

1 Stir together water and agave nectar in large glass measure.

2 Combine all-purpose flour, white whole wheat flour, yeast, and salt in food processor; pulse until mixed. With machine running, pour water–agave nectar mixture through feed tube; process until dough forms and pulls away from side of bowl, about 1 minute. Turn dough onto lightly floured surface and knead a few times or until smooth. Cover with clean kitchen towel and let rest 15 minutes.

3 Spray large baking sheet with nonstick spray. Lightly sprinkle work surface with flour. Divide dough in half. Roll one piece of dough into 10-inch round; with pizza cutter or knife, cut into 6 wedges. Starting at wide end, roll up each wedge and bend ends in to form crescent. Place seam side down, 2 inches apart, on prepared baking sheet. Repeat with remaining piece of dough, making total of 12 crescents. Cover rolls loosely with plastic wrap and let rise in warm place (80–85°F) until almost doubled in size, about 35 minutes.

4 Meanwhile, preheat oven to 375°F.

5 Remove plastic wrap; gently brush tops of rolls with egg wash and sprinkle with nigella seeds. Bake until rolls are golden brown, about 15 minutes. Transfer rolls to wire rack. Serve warm or at room temperature.

PER SERVING (1 roll): 74 Cal, 1 g Total Fat, 0 g Sat Fat, 0 g Trans Fat, 18 mg Chol, 251 mg Sod, 14 g Carb, 1 g Sugar, 1 g Fib, 3 g Prot, 8 mg Calc.

now try this

Nigella seeds, also called black onion seeds or black cumin seeds, come from a plant that boasts pale blue and white flowers and is native to south and southwest Asia. The seeds are often added to Armenian string cheese, a round pretzel-like Lebanese pastry called *kaak*, and sprinkled over Turkish flatbreads. Their flavor is reminiscent of cumin and charred onion.

big pan potato rolls with caraway salt

MAKES 24

PER SERVING

▲ **1 (8-ounce) russet potato, peeled and cut into 1-inch chunks**

3½ tablespoons unsalted butter

⅓ cup low-fat (1%) milk

1 tablespoon sugar

¾ teaspoon salt

1 envelope active dry yeast

⅔ cup whole wheat flour

2 cups all-purpose flour

1 teaspoon coarse sea salt or kosher salt

1 teaspoon caraway seeds

1 Put potato in saucepan with water to cover; bring to boil. Simmer until tender, 10–12 minutes. Drain, reserving ½ cup potato cooking liquid. Return potato to saucepan. Add 1½ tablespoons of butter and mash until smooth. Stir in milk, 2 teaspoons of sugar, and the salt. Transfer to large bowl of electric mixer fitted with paddle attachment.

2 Let reserved cooking liquid cool until warm (105–115°F). Stir in yeast and remaining 1 teaspoon sugar. Let stand until frothy; about 10 minutes. Stir into mashed potato. With mixer at medium speed, beat in whole wheat flour. Reduce speed; mix in all but about ¼ cup of all-purpose flour to form dough. Switch to dough hook. Knead, adding remaining ¼ cup flour, a little at a time, until dough is smooth but slightly sticky. Transfer to floured surface; knead 1 minute.

3 Lightly oil large bowl. Put dough in bowl and turn to coat. Cover bowl tightly with plastic wrap; let rise in refrigerator at least 8 hours or up to 12 hours.

4 Melt 1 tablespoon butter; use to coat 9 x 13-inch baking pan. Lightly flour work surface and large knife. Turn dough out onto work surface and gently press to deflate. Cut into quarters. Cut each piece of dough into 6 (1-ounce) pieces. With floured hands, roll each piece into rough ball and place in prepared pan, forming 6 rows of 4. Cover with towel. Let rise in warm place (80–85°F) until doubled in size, 1–2 hours.

5 Meanwhile, preheat oven to 375°F. Mix together coarse salt and caraway seeds. Melt remaining 1 tablespoon butter. Brush over rolls and sprinkle evenly with caraway salt. Bake until rolls are browned, 25–30 minutes. Serve warm or at room temperature.

PER SERVING (2 rolls): 76 Cal, 4 g Total Fat, 2 g Sat Fat, 0 g Trans Fat, 10 mg Chol, 310 mg Sod, 26 g Carb, 2 g Sugar, 2 g Fib, 4 g Prot, 18 mg Calc.

black skillet jalapeño corn bread

SERVES 16

3 PointsPlus® value

PER SERVING

▲ **1 cup yellow cornmeal**

1 cup all-purpose flour

3 tablespoons sugar

1 teaspoon baking powder

¾ teaspoon salt

½ teaspoon baking soda

1¼ cups low-fat buttermilk

▲ **1 large egg**

▲ **2 large egg whites**

2 tablespoons canola oil

▲ **1 cup frozen corn kernels**

▲ **2 large jalapeño peppers, seeded and finely chopped**

1 Preheat oven to 400°F. Spray 9-inch cast-iron or heavy ovenproof skillet with nonstick spray.

2 Whisk together cornmeal, flour, sugar, baking powder, salt, and baking soda in large bowl. Whisk together buttermilk, egg, egg whites, and oil in medium bowl. Stir in corn and jalapeños. Add buttermilk mixture to cornmeal mixture, stirring until combined well. Pour batter into prepared skillet and spread evenly.

3 Bake until corn bread is golden brown and toothpick inserted into center comes out clean, about 30 minutes. Let cool slightly in pan on wire rack. Cut into 16 pieces and serve warm.

PER SERVING (*1 piece*): 111 Cal, 2 g Total Fat, 1 g Sat Fat, 0 g Trans Fat, 14 mg Chol, 214 mg Sod, 19 g Carb, 3 g Sugar, 1 g Fib, 3 g Prot, 32 mg Calc.

for your info

The amount of heat in jalapeños varies from medium to very hot. If the peppers you purchase only have a medium amount of heat, add several drops of Tabasco to the buttermilk mixture.

BLACK SKILLET JALAPEÑO
CORN BREAD

chapter 4

the main course

beef, pork, and lamb; chicken, game hen, and turkey; fish and shellfish; vegetarian

spicy t-bones with roasted cherry tomato branches

SERVES 6

2 tablespoons amber or dark agave nectar

1 canned chipotle pepper in adobo, minced

2 large garlic cloves, minced

Finely grated zest of ½ orange

2 teaspoons chili powder

2 teaspoons ground cumin

2 teaspoons onion powder

1 teaspoon dried oregano

1 teaspoon salt

2 (1½-pound) lean T-bone steaks, ½ inch thick, trimmed

▲ 2 (8-ounce) containers cherry tomatoes on branches or 48 cherry tomatoes (about 2 pints)

¼ teaspoon black pepper

1 To make rub, stir together agave nectar, chipotle, garlic, orange zest, chili powder, cumin, onion powder, oregano, and ¾ teaspoon of salt in small bowl. Rub spice mixture on both sides of steaks. Put steaks on plate; cover and refrigerate at least 1 hour or up to 6 hours.

2 Meanwhile, place oven racks in middle and upper third of oven and preheat to 425°F. Spray rimmed baking sheet with olive oil nonstick spray.

3 Place tomato branches on prepared baking sheet and spray with olive oil nonstick spray; sprinkle with remaining ¼ teaspoon salt and the black pepper. Roast on middle rack until tomatoes soften, about 20 minutes. Snip branches into 6 portions, if necessary, and keep warm.

4 Preheat broiler. Spray broiler rack with nonstick spray.

5 Place steaks on prepared broiler rack and broil 5 inches from heat until instant-read thermometer inserted into side of steak registers 140°F for medium, about 5 minutes per side. Transfer steaks to cutting board and let stand 5 minutes. Cut each steak into 3 portions. Serve with tomatoes.

PER SERVING (*1 piece steak and about 8 cherry tomatoes*): 351 Cal, 15 g Total Fat, 5 g Sat Fat, 0 g Trans Fat, 94 mg Chol, 547 mg Sod, 6 g Carb, 2 g Sugar, 2 g Fib, 45 g Prot, 51 mg Calc.

now try this

Agave nectar, extracted from the blue agave plant, is about 1½ times sweeter than sugar or honey. Light agave nectar is very mild so is best used in beverages and delicate dishes. Amber agave has a medium amount of flavor with caramel notes and is recommended for dishes that are more boldly flavored and in baking. Dark agave nectar's rich caramel flavor makes it ideal for topping pancakes and French toast. Look for it in your supermarket.

BEEF FILLET STEAKS WITH TOMATO, CORN, AND BLACK BEAN SALSA

beef fillet steaks with tomato, corn, and black bean salsa

SERVES 4

8 PointsPlus® value

PER SERVING

- ▲ 1 (15½-ounce) can black beans, rinsed and drained
- ▲ 2 tomatoes, seeded and chopped
- ▲ ½ cup fresh corn kernels (about 1 ear of corn)
- ▲ 2 scallions, thinly sliced

  ½ Hass avocado, peeled, pitted, and chopped

  3 tablespoons chopped fresh cilantro

  2 tablespoons lime juice
- ▲ ½–1 jalapeño pepper, seeded and minced

  1 garlic clove, minced

  ½ teaspoon salt
- ▲ 1 (1-pound) lean beef tenderloin, trimmed

  ½ teaspoon black pepper

  2 teaspoons olive oil

1 To make salsa, mix together beans, tomatoes, corn, scallions, avocado, cilantro, lime juice, jalapeño, garlic, and ¼ teaspoon of salt in serving bowl.

2 Cut beef lengthwise (along grain) into 4 thick slices. Place each slice between two pieces of plastic wrap and lightly pound with meat mallet or bottom of heavy saucepan. Sprinkle with remaining ¼ teaspoon salt and the black pepper.

3 Heat oil in large cast-iron or heavy nonstick skillet over medium-high heat. Add beef and cook until instant-read thermometer inserted into side of steak registers 140°F for medium, about 3 minutes per side. Serve with salsa.

PER SERVING (*1 piece beef and about 1 cup salsa*): 332 Cal, 12 g Total Fat, 3 g Sat Fat, 0 g Trans Fat, 67 mg Chol, 689 mg Sod, 24 g Carb, 3 g Sugar, 7 g Fib, 31 g Prot, 67 mg Calc.

stay on track

The flavorful fiber-packed salsa is also a great match for other lean proteins, including shrimp and skinless boneless chicken breasts (4 ounces of grilled or broiled shrimp per serving has a *PointsPlus* value of *2* while a 3-ounce grilled or broiled skinless boneless chicken breast per serving has a *PointsPlus* value of *3*).

chuck-wagon sirloin with coffee barbecue sauce

SERVES 6

2 teaspoons olive oil

2 large garlic cloves, minced

½ cup strong brewed coffee

¼ cup ketchup

¼ cup steak sauce

¼ cup honey

¼ cup distilled white vinegar

1 tablespoon chili powder

2 teaspoons ground cumin

½–1 teaspoon hot pepper sauce

▲ 1 (1¼-pound) lean strip steak, 1¼ inches thick, trimmed

¼ teaspoon salt

1 Heat oil in medium saucepan over medium heat. Add garlic and cook, stirring, until golden, about 2 minutes. Add coffee, ketchup, steak sauce, honey, vinegar, chili powder, cumin, and pepper sauce. Bring to boil, stirring occasionally. Reduce heat to low and simmer, stirring frequently, until sauce is thickened, about 20 minutes.

2 Meanwhile, spray grill rack with nonstick spray. Preheat grill to medium or prepare medium fire.

3 Sprinkle steak with salt. Place on grill rack and grill 8 minutes per side. Brush with sauce and grill 3 minutes. Turn steak over and brush with sauce; grill until instant-read thermometer inserted into center of steak registers 140°F for medium, about 3 minutes longer. Transfer to cutting board and let stand 5 minutes; cut steak on diagonal into 24 very thin slices. Serve with sauce.

PER SERVING (*4 slices steak and about 2 tablespoons sauce*): 195 Cal, 5 g Total Fat, 1 g Sat Fat, 0 g Trans Fat, 52 mg Chol, 394 mg Sod, 17 g Carb, 15 g Sugar, 1 g Fib, 22 g Prot, 23 mg Calc.

stay on track

Turn this relatively low *PointsPlus* value main dish into a complete meal by serving with a side of corn on the cob and grilled zucchini sprinkled with sliced fresh basil (1 medium ear of corn per serving will increase the *PointsPlus* value by *2*).

spicy tangerine beef

SERVES 4

▲ 3 tangerines or navel oranges

▲ 1 pound lean strip sirloin steak, trimmed and thinly sliced

3 tablespoons reduced-sodium soy sauce

3 large garlic cloves, minced

1 tablespoon minced peeled fresh ginger

1 teaspoon cornstarch

½ teaspoon red pepper flakes or to taste

1 tablespoon canola oil

▲ 1 bunch broccoli, cut into small florets (about 5 cups)

▲ 4 large scallions, cut into 2-inch lengths

▲ 1 red or orange bell pepper, thinly sliced

1 With vegetable peeler, remove 8 (3-inch) strips of zest from tangerines; set aside. With knife, cut away remaining peel and pith from 1 tangerine. Holding tangerine over small bowl to catch juice, cut along each side of membranes to release each segment, allowing it to fall into bowl along with any juice. Repeat with second tangerine. Squeeze enough juice from remaining tangerine to equal ⅓ cup; set aside.

2 Combine steak, soy sauce, garlic, and ginger in large zip-close plastic bag. Squeeze out air and seal bag; turn to coat beef. Refrigerate, turning bag occasionally, about 30 minutes.

3 Stir together reserved tangerine juice, cornstarch, and pepper flakes in cup; set aside.

4 Heat wok over high heat until drop of water sizzles in pan. Add oil and swirl to coat pan. Remove beef from marinade; discard marinade. Add beef to wok and stir-fry until lightly browned, about 3 minutes. With slotted spoon, transfer beef to plate. Add broccoli, scallions, bell pepper, and orange strips to wok; stir-fry until broccoli is bright green, about 3 minutes.

5 Re-stir cornstarch mixture. Add to wok and stir-fry until sauce bubbles and thickens, about 1 minute. Return beef to wok and stir-fry until heated through, about 1 minute longer. Discard orange strips.

PER SERVING (1¾ cups): 146 Cal, 4 g Total Fat, 0 g Sat Fat, 0 g Trans Fat, 0 mg Chol, 456 mg Sod, 25 g Carb, 11 g Sugar, 6 g Fib, 6 g Prot, 115 mg Calc.

salty, sour, bitter, and sweet beef-noodle salad

SERVES 4

- ▲ **8 ounces whole wheat capellini, broken into 3-inch lengths**
- ▲ **1 head Boston lettuce, torn into bite-size pieces**
- ▲ **2 cups bean sprouts**
- ▲ **1 large tomato, seeded and chopped**
- ▲ **1 cup matchstick-cut or coarsely grated carrots**
- **1 cup lightly packed fresh cilantro leaves**
- **¼ cup lightly packed fresh mint leaves, torn**
- **3 tablespoons lime juice**
- **3 tablespoons packed brown sugar**
- **3 tablespoons reduced-sodium soy sauce**
- **2 teaspoons grated peeled fresh ginger**
- **2 teaspoons Asian fish sauce**
- **2 teaspoons canola oil**
- **½–1 teaspoon Thai red curry paste**
- ▲ **¾ pound lean round steak, trimmed and cut into ¼ x 2-inch slices**
- **3 tablespoons dry-roasted peanuts, chopped**

1 Cook pasta according to package directions, omitting salt if desired. Drain and rinse under cold running water; drain again. Transfer to large bowl. Add lettuce, bean sprouts, tomato, carrots, ½ cup of cilantro, and the mint. (Do not toss.)

2 To make dressing, whisk together lime juice, brown sugar, soy sauce, ginger, fish sauce, oil, and curry paste in small bowl. Put beef in medium bowl. Add 2 tablespoons of dressing and toss to coat well. Reserve remaining dressing.

3 Spray large cast-iron or heavy nonstick skillet with nonstick spray and set over medium-high heat. Add half of beef and cook, stirring occasionally, until browned and just cooked through, about 2 minutes. Transfer beef to large plate. Wipe skillet dry with paper towels. Cook remaining beef; add to beef on plate. Let beef cool slightly.

4 Drizzle reserved dressing over pasta-vegetable mixture and toss until coated well. Mound evenly onto 4 plates. Arrange one-fourth of beef on top of each serving of salad; sprinkle evenly with remaining ½ cup cilantro and the peanuts.

PER SERVING (*about 3 cups*): 479 Cal, 13 g Total Fat, 3 g Sat Fat, 0 g Trans Fat, 36 mg Chol, 740 mg Sod, 65 g Carb, 18 g Sugar, 11 g Fib, 33 g Prot, 85 mg Calc.

slow-cooker provençal-style stew

SERVES 6

6 PointsPlus® value

PER SERVING

▲ **1 pound boneless lean beef bottom round, trimmed and cut into 1-inch chunks**

▲ **1 large onion, coarsely chopped**

▲ **3 carrots, thickly sliced**

6 garlic cloves, minced

▲ **1 (28-ounce) can diced tomatoes**

1 cup dry red wine

4 (3-inch) strips orange zest

1 teaspoon dried thyme

¾ teaspoon salt

¼–½ teaspoon piment d'Espelette or black pepper

2 bay leaves

1 tablespoon extra-virgin olive oil

▲ **1 pound mixed mushrooms, such as cremini and white, halved**

½ cup niçoise olives

1 Combine beef, onion, carrots, garlic, tomatoes, wine, orange strips, thyme, salt, piment d'Espelette, and bay leaves in 5- or 6-quart slow cooker. Cover and cook until beef is fork-tender, 4–5 hours on high or 8–10 hours on low.

2 About 20 minutes before cooking time is up, heat oil in large nonstick skillet over medium heat. Add mushrooms and cook, stirring, until browned and liquid is evaporated, about 8 minutes.

3 Stir mushrooms and olives into stew. Cover and cook on high until mushrooms are tender, about 10 minutes longer. Remove orange strips and bay leaves; discard.

PER SERVING (*about 1½ cups*): 244 Cal, 9 g Total Fat, 2 g Sat Fat, 0 g Trans Fat, 59 mg Chol, 509 mg Sod, 12 g Carb, 4 g Sugar, 2 g Fib, 22 g Prot, 62 mg Calc.

now try this

Piment d'Espelette is a variety of pepper grown in the small region of Espelette in France. It has an unusual light, sweet spiciness. This pepper, originally from Mexico, was brought to France in the sixteenth century and used medicinally. Piment d'Espelette is a key ingredient in the Basque dish piperade.

tomato-beef ragu with ricotta and mint

SERVES 4

11
PointsPlus©
value

PER SERVING

2 teaspoons olive oil

▲ 1 pound ground lean beef (7% fat or less)

▲ 1 onion, chopped

▲ 1 red bell pepper, chopped

▲ 1 large celery stalk, quartered lengthwise and sliced

4 large garlic cloves, minced

▲ 1 (28-ounce) can fire-roasted diced tomatoes

8 fresh basil leaves, thinly sliced

½ teaspoon dried oregano

¼ teaspoon black pepper

¼ teaspoon red pepper flakes

▲ 8 ounces whole wheat fettuccine

▲ ¼ cup fat-free ricotta cheese, drained

2 tablespoons chopped fresh mint

1 Heat oil in large nonstick skillet over medium heat. Add beef and cook, breaking it apart with wooden spoon, until lightly browned, about 4 minutes. Stir in onion, bell pepper, celery, and garlic; cook, stirring occasionally, until vegetables are softened, about 5 minutes.

2 Stir in tomatoes, basil, oregano, black pepper, and pepper flakes; bring to boil. Reduce heat and simmer, stirring occasionally, until slightly thickened, about 15 minutes.

3 Meanwhile, cook pasta according to package directions, omitting salt if desired. Drain and keep warm.

4 Divide pasta among 4 bowls and top evenly with ragu. Spoon 1-tablespoon dollop of ricotta on top of each serving and sprinkle with mint.

PER SERVING (*about 2 cups*): 453 Cal, 9 g Total Fat, 3 g Sat Fat, 0 g Trans Fat, 70 mg Chol, 570 mg Sod, 59 g Carb, 13 g Sugar, 11 g Fib, 36 g Prot, 140 mg Calc.

stay on track

A refreshing Italian-style salad of thinly sliced fennel, sliced radishes, arugula, and fresh orange segments dressed with lemon juice and a sprinkling of black pepper is a great way to begin your meal without increasing the *PointsPlus* value.

TOMATO-BEEF RAGU WITH RICOTTA AND MINT AND PARMESAN AND BLACK PEPPER GREEN BEANS, p.179

winter's best beef and barley stew

SERVES 8

▲ 1 celery root, peeled and cut into ¾-inch chunks

▲ 4 carrots, thickly sliced

▲ 3 parsnips, thickly sliced

▲ 2 onions, sliced

1 teaspoon salt

½ teaspoon black pepper

1 tablespoon + 1 teaspoon olive oil

1½ pounds boneless lean beef chuck, trimmed and cut into 1-inch chunks

4 large garlic cloves, minced

▲ 5½ cups reduced-sodium beef broth

▲ 3 large plum tomatoes, coarsely chopped

1 tablespoon chopped fresh rosemary

▲ 8 ounces white mushrooms, thickly sliced

▲ 1 cup pearl barley, rinsed

1 Preheat oven to 425°F. Spray large rimmed baking sheet with olive oil nonstick spray.

2 Combine celery root, carrots, parsnips, and onions on prepared baking sheet; spray with nonstick spray and sprinkle with ½ teaspoon of salt and ¼ teaspoon of pepper; toss until coated evenly. Spread vegetables to form even layer. Roast, stirring occasionally, until vegetables begin to brown and are just tender, about 30 minutes.

3 Meanwhile, heat oil in Dutch oven over medium-high heat. Cook beef, in batches, until browned, about 4 minutes per batch, transferring beef to plate as it is browned. Add garlic to pot and cook, stirring, until golden, about 1 minute.

4 Return beef to Dutch oven. Add broth, tomatoes, rosemary, and remaining ½ teaspoon salt and ¼ teaspoon pepper; bring to boil. Reduce heat and simmer, partially covered, 45 minutes.

5 Stir mushrooms and barley into pot; bring to boil. Reduce heat and simmer, covered, stirring occasionally, 15 minutes. Stir in roasted vegetables and bring to boil. Reduce heat and simmer, covered, until beef is fork-tender and barley is softened, about 15 minutes longer, adding water if stew seems too thick.

PER SERVING (*generous 1 cup*): 331 Cal, 8 g Total Fat, 2 g Sat Fat, 0 g Trans Fat, 36 mg Chol, 424 mg Sod, 41 g Carb, 9 g Sugar, 8 g Fib, 26 g Prot, 81 mg Calc.

simply peachy pork roast with lavender and mustard

SERVES 4

PER SERVING

3 large garlic cloves, minced

1 tablespoon chopped fresh thyme

½ teaspoon salt

¼ teaspoon black pepper

▲ 1 (1¼-pound) boneless lean center-cut pork loin roast, trimmed

¼ cup peach or orange preserves

2 tablespoons country-style Dijon mustard

1 teaspoon fresh or dried lavender buds

1 Preheat oven to 400°F. Spray roasting pan with nonstick spray.

2 Stir together garlic, thyme, salt, and pepper in small bowl. Spray pork with olive oil nonstick spray; rub thyme mixture all over pork. Place pork in prepared pan and roast 30 minutes.

3 Meanwhile, stir together preserves, mustard, and lavender in small bowl; brush all over pork. Roast until instant-read thermometer inserted into center of pork registers 140°F for medium, about 10 minutes longer. Transfer to cutting board and let stand 10 minutes. Cut into 12 slices.

PER SERVING (*3 slices pork*): 240 Cal, 7 g Total Fat, 2 g Sat Fat, 0 g Trans Fat, 83 mg Chol, 527 mg Sod, 15 g Carb, 12 g Sugar, 0 g Fib, 27 g Prot, 30 mg Calc.

now try this

Dried lavender buds are found in specialty food stores, spice and herb shops, and online. They are often used in Provençal stews and braises, as lavender is native to that region of France. Lavender's unique aroma and flavor adds a bit of the exotic to simply prepared dishes. If you happen to have fresh lavender growing in your garden, use it here.

peppered pork tenderloin with redeye sauce

SERVES 4

1 tablespoon paprika

1 teaspoon dried thyme

½ + ⅛ teaspoon black pepper

½ teaspoon salt

¼ teaspoon mustard powder

▲ 1 (1-pound) lean pork tenderloin, trimmed

1 tablespoon canola oil

1 thin slice prosciutto, chopped

▲ ¼ cup finely chopped onion

▲ 1 cup reduced-sodium chicken broth

¼ cup strong brewed coffee

1½ tablespoons packed brown sugar

1 tablespoon cider vinegar

1 Preheat oven to 400°F.

2 To make spice rub, on sheet of wax paper, mix together paprika, thyme, ½ teaspoon of pepper, the salt, and mustard powder. Roll pork in spice mixture until coated evenly.

3 Heat 2 teaspoons of oil in large cast-iron or other heavy nonstick ovenproof skillet over medium-high heat. Tuck thin end of tenderloin under so it is an even thickness and place in skillet. Cook until lightly browned on all sides, about 5 minutes.

4 Transfer skillet to oven and roast until instant-read thermometer inserted into center of tenderloin registers 140°F for medium, about 20 minutes. Transfer pork to cutting board and let stand 5 minutes. Cut into 16 slices.

5 Meanwhile, to make sauce, heat medium nonstick skillet over medium heat. Add prosciutto and cook, stirring, until crispy, about 4 minutes. Add remaining 1 teaspoon oil and the onion; cook, stirring, until onion is softened, about 5 minutes. Add broth, coffee, brown sugar, vinegar, and remaining ⅛ teaspoon pepper; bring to simmer. Cook, stirring occasionally, until sauce is reduced to ½ cup, about 10 minutes. Serve with pork.

PER SERVING (*4 slices pork and 2 tablespoons sauce*): 214 Cal, 9 g Total Fat, 2 g Sat Fat, 0 g Trans Fat, 65 mg Chol, 455 mg Sod, 9 g Carb, 5 g Sugar, 1 g Fib, 25 g Prot, 25 mg Calc.

szechuan pork and ginger

SERVES 6

8 PointsPlus® value
PER SERVING

¼ cup water

3 tablespoons reduced-sodium soy sauce

1 teaspoon chili-garlic sauce or to taste

1 teaspoon cornstarch

1 tablespoon canola oil

▲ 1 pound boneless lean pork loin, trimmed and cut into ¼ x 1-inch slices

▲ 1 orange bell pepper, thinly sliced

▲ 4 ounces green beans, trimmed and cut into thirds

▲ 6 scallions, cut into 2-inch lengths

2 tablespoons grated peeled fresh ginger

3 large garlic cloves, minced

▲ 1 (15-ounce) can straw mushrooms, drained

▲ 1 cup drained canned corn

▲ 3 cups hot cooked brown rice

1 Stir together water, soy sauce, chili-garlic sauce, and cornstarch in cup; set aside.

2 Heat wok over medium-high heat until drop of water sizzles in pan. Add 1 ½ teaspoons of oil and swirl to coat pan. Add pork, in batches, and stir-fry until browned and cooked through, about 4 minutes, transferring pork to plate as it is browned.

3 Add remaining 1 ½ teaspoons oil to wok. Add bell pepper, green beans, scallions, ginger, and garlic; stir-fry until beans are crisp-tender, about 3 minutes. Add mushrooms and corn; stir-fry until heated through, about 1 minute longer. Return pork to wok.

4 Re-stir cornstarch mixture and add to wok. Stir-fry until sauce bubbles and thickens, about 2 minutes. Serve with rice.

PER SERVING (1½ cups pork mixture and ½ cup rice): 305 Cal, 8 g Total Fat, 2 g Sat Fat, 0 g Trans Fat, 44 mg Chol, 699 mg Sod, 37 g Carb, 3 g Sugar, 6 g Fib, 21 g Prot, 53 mg Calc.

stay on track

Keep the *PointsPlus* value the same while contributing flavor, crunch, and a variety of vitamins and minerals. Add 2 cups of small broccoli florets to the wok along with the vegetables in step 3.

smoky pork in adobo sauce

SERVES 6

8
PointsPlus®
value

PER SERVING

1 tablespoon olive oil

▲ 1 pound boneless lean pork loin, trimmed and cut into ½-inch pieces

▲ 1 onion, chopped

▲ 2 red bell peppers, chopped

3 large garlic cloves, minced

▲ 1 (14½-ounce) can petite diced tomatoes

1 tablespoon chopped canned chipotle pepper in adobo or to taste

2 teaspoons chili powder

2 teaspoons ground cumin

1 teaspoon dried oregano

½ teaspoon salt

▲ 1 (15½-ounce) can black beans, rinsed and drained

▲ 3 cups hot cooked brown rice

▲ 2 cups plain air-popped popcorn

1 Heat 1½ teaspoons of oil in large nonstick Dutch oven over medium heat. Add pork, in batches, and cook, stirring occasionally, until lightly browned, about 6 minutes, transferring to plate as it is browned.

2 Add remaining 1½ teaspoons oil to pot. Add onion, bell peppers, and garlic; cook, stirring occasionally, until softened, about 5 minutes. Stir in tomatoes, chipotle, chili powder, cumin, oregano, and salt; bring to boil. Add beans and pork with any accumulated juices. Reduce heat and simmer, covered, until pork is tender, about 10 minutes longer.

3 Divide rice and pork mixture among 6 bowls. Top with popcorn.

PER SERVING (about 1 cup pork mixture, ½ cup rice, and ⅓ cup popcorn): 337 Cal, 8 g Total Fat, 2 g Sat Fat, 0 g Trans Fat, 44 mg Chol, 638 mg Sod, 44 g Carb, 5 g Sugar, 7 g Fib, 22 g Prot, 78 mg Calc.

for your info

The popcorn adds welcome crunch and a bit of whimsy to this dish.

**SMOKY PORK IN
ADOBO SAUCE**

grilled rack of lamb with tarragon and charred tomatoes

SERVES 4

½ cup fresh whole wheat bread crumbs (about 1 slice bread)

¼ cup chopped fresh parsley

2 teaspoons chopped fresh tarragon

1 small garlic clove, minced

1 (8-rib) rack of lamb, trimmed and frenched

½ teaspoon salt

¼ + ⅛ teaspoon black pepper

2 tablespoons Dijon mustard

▲ 4 tomatoes, cut crosswise in half

1 Mix together bread crumbs, 3 tablespoons of parsley, the tarragon, and garlic in small bowl. Spray with olive oil nonstick spray and toss until crumbs are just moistened. Stir in a bit of water if mixture seems dry.

2 Spray grill rack with nonstick spray. Preheat grill to medium-high or prepare medium-high fire.

3 Sprinkle lamb with ¼ teaspoon of salt and ¼ teaspoon of pepper. Place lamb, meaty side down, on grill rack and grill until nicely browned, about 5 minutes per side. Transfer lamb to plate. Brush mustard over meaty side of lamb, then press herb-crumb mixture over mustard; lightly spray herb-crumb mixture with olive oil nonstick spray. Return lamb, crumb side up, to grill and cook until instant-read thermometer inserted into center of lamb (not touching bone) registers 140°F for medium, about 10 minutes (do not turn).

4 Transfer lamb to cutting board and cover loosely with foil.

5 Spray cut side of tomatoes with nonstick spray. Sprinkle with remaining ¼ teaspoon salt and ⅛ teaspoon pepper. Place tomatoes, cut side down, on grill rack and grill until nicely charred and softened, about 5 minutes.

6 With sharp knife, slice between every other bone, making 4 double chops. Sprinkle tomatoes with remaining 1 tablespoon parsley and serve alongside lamb.

PER SERVING (*1 double lamb chop and 2 tomato halves*): 406 Cal, 15 g Total Fat, 6 g Sat Fat, 0 g Trans Fat, 172 mg Chol, 640 mg Sod, 14 g Carb, 5 g Sugar, 3 g Fib, 50 g Prot, 0 82 mg Calc.

basque-style lamb with bell peppers and olives

SERVES 4

PER SERVING

▲ **1 red bell pepper, halved and seeded**

▲ **1 yellow bell pepper, halved and seeded**

½ teaspoon olive oil

▲ **1 onion, sliced**

3 large garlic cloves, minced

▲ **½ cup diced canned or fresh tomatoes**

12 pitted Kalamata olives, chopped

½ teaspoon salt

½ teaspoon piment d'Espelette (see tip page 115) or ⅛ teaspoon cayenne

1 tablespoon chopped fresh parsley

4 (¼-pound) lean rib lamb chops, about ¾ inch thick, trimmed

▲ **2 cups hot cooked whole wheat couscous**

1 Spray grill rack with nonstick spray. Preheat grill to medium-high or prepare medium-high fire.

2 Place bell peppers on grill rack and grill, turning occasionally, until tender, about 10 minutes. Transfer peppers to cutting board. When cool enough to handle, cut into 1-inch pieces; set aside. (Leave grill on.)

3 Coat large nonstick skillet with oil and set over medium heat. Add onion and garlic; cook, stirring, until onion is softened, about 5 minutes. Add bell peppers, tomatoes, olives, ¼ teaspoon of salt, and ¼ teaspoon of piment d'Espelette. Cook, covered, stirring occasionally, until flavors are blended, about 10 minutes. Remove skillet from heat. Stir in parsley; keep warm.

4 Sprinkle lamb chops with remaining ¼ teaspoon salt and ¼ teaspoon piment d'Espelette. Place on grill rack and grill, turning occasionally, until instant-read thermometer inserted into side of chop registers 140°F for medium, about 10 minutes. Transfer lamb to platter and spoon bell pepper sauce over and around. Serve with couscous.

PER SERVING (*1 lamb chop, about ⅓ cup sauce, and ½ cup couscous*): 313 Cal, 11 g Total Fat, 3 g Sat Fat, 0 g Trans Fat, 86 mg Chol, 610 mg Sod, 26 g Carb, 6 g Sugar, 5 g Fib, 28 g Prot, 52 mg Calc.

stay on track

For an extra dose of fiber, serve a bowl of steamed whole green beans alongside the chops, and end the meal on a sweet note by serving a bowl of fresh seasonal fruit.

GRILLED CHEESE-CRUSTED LAMB
CHOPS WITH HERBED POTATOES

grilled cheese-crusted lamb chops with herbed potatoes

SERVES 4

▲ **1 pound red and/or white small potatoes, scrubbed and halved**

2 tablespoons Dijon mustard

1 teaspoon dried thyme or oregano

½ teaspoon black pepper

8 (3-ounce) lean lamb rib chops, trimmed

¼ cup grated Grana Padano or Parmesan cheese

¼ cup whole wheat panko (Japanese bread crumbs)

2 tablespoons chopped mixed fresh herbs, such as dill, parsley, and mint

1 Combine potatoes with about ½ inch water to cover in large saucepan; bring to boil. Reduce heat and simmer, covered, until tender, about 12 minutes, Drain and return to saucepan; keep warm.

2 Meanwhile, stir together mustard, thyme, and ¼ teaspoon of pepper in cup. Brush on one side of each lamb chop.

3 Mix together Grana Padano and panko on small plate. Press mustard-coated side of each chop into cheese mixture, pressing lightly so it adheres. Lightly spray cheese mixture with olive oil nonstick spray.

4 Heat large nonstick skillet over medium heat. Add chops, cheese side down, and cook until crusty and lightly browned, about 4 minutes. Turn and cook until instant-read thermometer inserted into side of chop registers 140°F for medium, about 4 minutes longer.

5 Spray potatoes with olive oil nonstick spray. Add fresh herbs and remaining ¼ teaspoon pepper; cook, stirring, over medium-high heat until potatoes are heated through, about 2 minutes. Serve with lamb.

PER SERVING (*2 lamb chops and ¼ of potatoes*): 375 Cal, 12 g Total Fat, 5 g Sat Fat, 0 g Trans Fat, 134 mg Chol, 360 mg Sod, 25 g Carb, 1 g Sugar, 3 g Fib, 40 g Prot, 92 mg Calc.

now try this

Grana Padano is a great grating cheese, just like Parmesan. It's flavor is subtler, however, as it isn't as salty. Grana Padano is a good cheese to use when you want the flavors of the other ingredients to shine through.

charred lamb kebabs with yellow rice

SERVES 4

▲ **1 pound boneless lean leg of lamb, trimmed and cut into 1-inch chunks**

2½ teaspoons canola oil

2–3 teaspoons curry powder

¾ teaspoon salt

▲ **1 onion, chopped + 1 onion, cut into thin wedges**

▲ **1 cup brown basmati rice**

▲ **2¼ cups reduced-sodium vegetable broth**

¼ teaspoon ground turmeric

▲ **16 cherry tomatoes**

¼ cup coarsely chopped fresh mint or cilantro

1 Toss together lamb, 2 teaspoons of oil, the curry powder, and salt in large bowl until coated evenly. Refrigerate.

2 To make rice, heat remaining ½ teaspoon oil in medium nonstick saucepan over medium heat. Add chopped onion and cook, stirring, until softened, 5 minutes. Add rice and cook, stirring constantly, until lightly toasted, 2–3 minutes. Add broth and turmeric; bring to boil. Reduce heat and simmer, covered, until rice is tender, 40–45 minutes. Remove saucepan from heat. Let stand 10 minutes, then fluff with fork; keep warm.

3 Spray broiler rack with nonstick spray and preheat broiler.

4 Meanwhile, thread lamb, onion wedges, and tomatoes alternately on 8 (12-inch) metal skewers. Place skewers on prepared broiler rack and broil 5 inches from heat, turning occasionally, until lamb is lightly charred and cooked through, about 10 minutes.

5 Spoon rice onto platter and sprinkle with mint. Top with lamb skewers.

PER SERVING (*2 skewers and ¾ cup rice*): 387 Cal, 11 g Total Fat, 3 g Sat Fat, 0 g Trans Fat, 83 mg Chol, 575 mg Sod, 46 g Carb, 8 g Sugar, 6 g Fib, 29 g Prot, 58 mg Calc.

spice-rubbed and vinegar-glazed chicken breasts

SERVES 6

¼ cup ketchup

2 tablespoons cider vinegar

3 tablespoons packed brown sugar

2 teaspoons smoked paprika

2 teaspoons chili powder

2 teaspoons ground cumin

2 teaspoons onion powder

1 teaspoon garlic powder

¾ teaspoon salt

½ teaspoon black pepper

▲ 6 (5-ounce) skinless boneless chicken breast halves

1 Spray grill rack with nonstick spray. Preheat grill to medium or prepare medium fire.

2 To make glaze, stir together ketchup, vinegar, and 1½ tablespoons of brown sugar in small bowl. To make spice rub, mix together paprika, chili powder, cumin, onion powder, garlic powder, salt, pepper, and remaining 1½ tablespoons brown sugar in another small bowl. Rub spice mixture all over chicken.

3 Place chicken on grill rack and grill 3 minutes per side. Turn chicken over and brush with half of glaze; grill 2 minutes. Turn and brush with remaining glaze; grill until instant-read thermometer inserted into thickest part of chicken registers 165°F, about 2 minutes longer.

PER SERVING (1 chicken breast): 203 Cal, 4 g Total Fat, 1 g Sat Fat, 0 g Trans Fat, 78 mg Chol, 484 mg Sod, 12 g Carb, 9 g Sugar, 1 g Fib, 29 g Prot, 35 mg Calc.

now try this

Smoked paprika, known as *pimentón* in Spain, is made from sweet or hot red peppers that have been slowly smoked over a wood fire before being ground. This process gives the paprika a rich smoky flavor. It is available in specialty food stores and online.

roasted chicken with caramelized meyer lemons

SERVES 6

▲ **3 small Meyer or regular lemons**

1 (3½-pound) chicken, without giblets

¾ teaspoon salt

½ teaspoon black pepper

4 small shallots, peeled

▲ **¾ cup reduced-sodium chicken broth**

1 tablespoon chopped fresh flat-leaf parsley

1 Preheat oven to 400°F. Spray medium roasting pan with nonstick spray.

2 Cut lemons crosswise in half. Cut 1 thin slice from each of 2 lemon halves. Place lemon halves, cut side down, and lemon slices in prepared roasting pan. Roast, turning slices, until caramelized, about 15 minutes. Remove lemon slices and set aside.

3 Meanwhile, rinse chicken inside and out under cold running water; pat dry with paper towels. Tuck wings under and tie legs together with kitchen string. Place chicken, breast side up, in roasting pan alongside lemon halves. Sprinkle chicken with ½ teaspoon of salt and ¼ teaspoon of pepper. Scatter shallots around chicken.

4 Roast chicken 30 minutes; add broth to pan. Roast until instant-read thermometer inserted into thigh (not touching bone) registers 165°F, about 30 minutes longer. Transfer chicken to cutting board and let stand 10 minutes.

5 To make sauce, when cool enough to handle, coarsely chop shallots. Coarsely chop slices of lemon. Transfer shallots and chopped lemon to mini food processor. Skim off fat from pan juices. Add pan juices and remaining ¼ teaspoon salt and ¼ teaspoon pepper to food processor; pulse until sauce is smooth.

6 Carve chicken. Transfer to platter and sprinkle with parsley. Place lemon halves on platter. Serve with sauce. Remove chicken skin before eating.

PER SERVING (⅙ of chicken, 1 lemon half, and 2 tablespoons sauce): 182 cal, 4 g Fat, 1 g Sat Fat, 0 g Trans Fat, 89 mg Chol, 402 mg Sod, 10 g Carb, 0 g Sugar, 3 g Fib, 29 g Prot, 59 mg Calc.

**ROASTED CHICKEN WITH
CARAMELIZED MEYER LEMONS**

chicken bouillabaisse with pimiento-garlic sauce

SERVES 4

6
PointsPlus©
value
PER SERVING

½ teaspoon olive oil

4 (6-ounce) chicken thighs, skinned and trimmed

▲ 1 small red onion, finely chopped

▲ ½ cup finely chopped fresh fennel

2 bay leaves

1 (3-inch) strip orange zest

4 large garlic cloves, minced

½ teaspoon fresh thyme leaves

¼ teaspoon salt

¼ teaspoon Sriracha (hot chile sauce; see tip page 27)

Pinch saffron threads, crumbled

▲ 1 (14½-ounce) can diced tomatoes

1 tablespoon chopped pimiento or roasted red pepper (not packed in oil)

¼ cup fat-free mayonnaise

1 tablespoon chopped fresh flat-leaf parsley

1 Coat medium nonstick skillet with oil and set over medium heat. Lightly spray chicken with olive oil nonstick spray. Add chicken to skillet and cook, turning occasionally, until lightly browned, about 10 minutes. With slotted spoon, transfer chicken to plate.

2 Add onion and fennel to skillet; cook, stirring frequently, until softened, about 5 minutes. Stir in bay leaves, orange zest, half of garlic, the thyme, ⅛ teaspoon of salt, ⅛ teaspoon of Sriracha, and the saffron; cook, stirring constantly, until fragrant, about 1 minute. Stir in tomatoes.

3 Return chicken to skillet; reduce heat and simmer, partially covered, turning chicken several times, until instant-read thermometer inserted into thigh (not touching bone) registers 165°F, about 30 minutes.

4 Transfer chicken to plate. Skim off and discard any fat from tomato mixture; bring to boil. Boil, stirring frequently, until thickened, about 5 minutes. Discard bay leaves and orange zest.

5 Meanwhile, to make pimiento-garlic sauce, combine pimiento and remaining garlic, ⅛ teaspoon salt, and ⅛ teaspoon Sriracha in mini food processor; process until very smooth. Add mayonnaise and pulse until combined. Transfer to serving bowl.

6 Place 1 chicken thigh on each of 4 plates. Spoon tomato-fennel sauce over chicken and sprinkle with parsley. Top each serving with dollop of pimiento-garlic sauce.

PER SERVING (1 chicken thigh, ¼ cup tomato-fennel sauce, and generous 1 tablespoon pimiento-garlic sauce): 249 cal, 11 g Fat, 3 g Sat Fat, 0 g Trans Fat, 87 mg Chol, 623 mg Sod, 11 g Carb, 6 g Sugar, 2 g Fib, 25 g Prot, 45 mg Calc.

restaurant-style hunter's chicken

SERVES 6

▲ **12 ounces whole wheat spaghetti**

▲ **6 (6-ounce) bone-in chicken breasts, skin removed**

½ teaspoon salt

¼ teaspoon black pepper

1 tablespoon olive oil

▲ **1 red bell pepper, thinly sliced**

▲ **1 green bell pepper, thinly sliced**

▲ **8 ounces portobello mushrooms, cut into ¾-inch chunks**

▲ **1 large onion, sliced**

3 large garlic cloves, minced

2 cups fat-free marinara sauce

1 tablespoon chopped fresh rosemary or oregano

¼–½ teaspoon red pepper flakes

¼ cup coarsely chopped fresh flat-leaf parsley

1 Cook pasta according to package directions, omitting salt if desired. Keep warm.

2 Sprinkle chicken with salt and black pepper.

3 Heat 2 teaspoons of oil in large nonstick skillet over medium heat. Add chicken, in batches, and cook until browned, about 5 minutes per side, transferring chicken to plate as it is browned.

4 Add remaining 1 teaspoon oil to skillet. Add bell peppers, mushrooms, onion, and garlic; cook, stirring, until vegetables are slightly softened, about 4 minutes.

5 Return chicken to skillet along with any accumulated juices. Add marinara sauce, rosemary, and pepper flakes; bring to boil. Reduce heat and simmer, covered, until chicken is cooked through and vegetables are tender, about 20 minutes. Divide chicken and pasta among 6 plates. Top with sauce and sprinkle with parsley.

PER SERVING (*1 chicken breast, ¾ cup vegetables with sauce, and 1 cup pasta*): 442 Cal, 7 g Total Fat, 1 g Sat Fat, 0 g Trans Fat, 76 mg Chol, 590 mg Sod, 57 g Carb, 5 g Sugar, 11 g Fib, 40 g Prot, 80 mg Calc.

for your info

Also known as chicken cacciatore, this popular chicken dish probably has as many variations as there are cooks who prepare it. In Italy, the region in which it is prepared often determines its ingredients. Our robust version is chock full of mushrooms and fresh herbs and is served over whole wheat pasta, so it is sure to be satisfying.

OVEN-FRIED CHICKEN WITH SRIRACHA-HONEY SAUCE

oven-fried chicken with sriracha-honey sauce

SERVES 4

½ cup whole wheat panko (Japanese bread crumbs)

2 tablespoons all-purpose flour

½ teaspoon salt

½ teaspoon black pepper

▲ ¾ cup plain fat-free yogurt

1 tablespoon dried sage

2 teaspoons dried rosemary, crumbled

½ teaspoon cayenne

▲ 4 (5-ounce) skinless boneless chicken breasts

2 tablespoons honey

2 tablespoons Sriracha (hot chile sauce; see tip page 27)

1 Preheat oven to 425°F. Line small baking sheet with parchment paper or foil and spray with olive oil nonstick spray.

2 Mix together panko, flour, salt, and black pepper in large shallow bowl. Mix together yogurt, sage, rosemary, and cayenne in another large shallow bowl. Dip chicken breasts, one at a time, in yogurt mixture, then coat with panko mixture.

3 Place chicken on prepared baking sheet; spray with nonstick spray. Bake, turning once, until crispy and cooked through, about 20 minutes.

4 Meanwhile, to make sauce, stir together honey and Sriracha in small bowl until blended. Drizzle over chicken just before serving.

PER SERVING (*1 chicken breast and 1 tablespoon sauce*): 250 Cal, 4 g Total Fat, 1 g Sat Fat, 0 g Trans Fat, 79 mg Chol, 588 mg Sod, 20 g Carb, 12 g Sugar, 1 g Fib, 33 g Prot, 125 mg Calc.

Keep the *PointsPlus* value the same while enjoying a generous serving of farm-fresh steamed green beans and a vitamin-rich salad of sliced tomato, red onion, and watercress dressed with balsamic vinegar.

pasilla pepper chicken mole

SERVES 6

10 PointsPlus® value

PER SERVING

▲ **3 dried pasilla chile peppers, seeded**

2 cups boiling water

▲ **2 cups reduced-sodium chicken broth**

6 (6-ounce) bone-in chicken thighs, skin removed and trimmed

1 teaspoon salt

¼ teaspoon black pepper

4 teaspoons olive oil

▲ **1 large onion, chopped**

3 garlic cloves, peeled

▲ **2 large plum tomatoes, chopped**

1 teaspoon ground cumin

¾ teaspoon dried oregano

½ teaspoon ground cinnamon

1 ounce semisweet chocolate, chopped

▲ **3 cups hot cooked brown rice**

¼ cup chopped fresh cilantro

1 Heat medium heavy skillet over medium-high heat. Add pasilla peppers and toast 30 seconds per side. Transfer to small bowl and cover with boiling water; let stand 20 minutes. Drain. Transfer chiles to blender. Add 1 cup of broth and puree; return chile mixture to bowl. Set aside.

2 Lightly spray chicken with olive oil nonstick spray; sprinkle with ½ teaspoon of salt and the black pepper. Heat nonstick Dutch oven over medium heat. Add 3 chicken thighs and cook until browned, about 4 minutes per side. Transfer to large plate; repeat with remaining chicken.

3 Add oil to Dutch oven (no need to wipe out pot.) Add onion and garlic; cook, stirring, until onion is softened, about 5 minutes. Stir in tomatoes and cook until softened, about 3 minutes. Add cumin, oregano, and cinnamon; cook until fragrant, about 30 seconds. Spoon tomato mixture into blender; add remaining 1 cup broth and puree.

4 Add pasilla mixture, pureed tomato mixture, and remaining ½ teaspoon salt to pot; cook, stirring, until thickened, about 6 minutes. Add chocolate, stirring, until melted, 1–2 minutes. Return chicken to pot and turn to coat with sauce. Simmer until chicken is cooked through, about 6 minutes longer.

5 Transfer chicken and sauce to platter or large deep serving bowl. Spoon rice into serving bowl and sprinkle with cilantro.

PER SERVING (*1 chicken thigh, ¼ cup sauce, and ½ cup rice*): 369 Cal, 14 g Total Fat, 4 g Sat Fat, 0 g Trans Fat, 86 mg Chol, 501 mg Sod, 33 g Carb, 4 g Sugar, 4 g Fib, 29 g Prot, 48 mg Calc.

now try this

The **dried pasilla pepper**, also called *chile negro*, meaning "little raisin," is a dried chilaca pepper. It is dark brown, wrinkled, elongated, and about 5 inches long. Pasilla peppers are a *must* ingredient when preparing an authentic mole.

slow-cooker french country–style chicken

SERVES 6

6 (6-ounce) bone-in chicken thighs, skin removed and trimmed

½ teaspoon salt

¼ teaspoon black pepper

▲ **1½ cups shredded green cabbage**

▲ **1 onion, chopped**

▲ **8 ounces white mushrooms, thickly sliced**

3 large garlic cloves, peeled

1½ cups dry red wine

2 tablespoons tomato paste

1½ teaspoons herbes de Provence (see tip page 31) or dried thyme

⅓ cup water

2 tablespoons all-purpose flour

1 Spray chicken with olive oil nonstick spray; sprinkle with salt and pepper. Heat large nonstick skillet over medium heat. Add chicken and cook, turning, until browned, about 10 minutes. Transfer to 5- or 6-quart slow cooker.

2 Add cabbage and onion to skillet. Cook, stirring, until onion is softened, about 5 minutes. Add mushrooms and cook, stirring, until slightly softened, about 4 minutes. Add cabbage-mushroom mixture and garlic to slow cooker.

3 Whisk together wine, tomato paste, and herbes de Provence in medium bowl until blended well, then pour over chicken. Cover and cook until chicken is fork-tender, 4–6 hours on high or 8–10 hours on low. With slotted spoon, transfer chicken to deep platter. Keep warm.

4 Whisk together water and flour in small bowl until smooth. Whisk in about ¼ cup of hot stew liquid until blended, then stir flour mixture into slow cooker. Cover and cook on high until mixture simmers and thickens, about 15 minutes.

PER SERVING (*1 chicken thigh and ½ cup vegetables with sauce*): 275 Cal, 10 g Total Fat, 3 g Sat Fat, 0 g Trans Fat, 86 mg Chol, 326 mg Sod, 9 g Carb, 3 g Sugar, 1 g Fib, 25 g Prot, 43 mg Calc.

apricot and mustard–glazed cornish hens

SERVES 4

¼ cup + 1 tablespoon apricot preserves

1 tablespoon country-style Dijon mustard

1 tablespoon chopped fresh rosemary

½ teaspoon salt

¼ teaspoon black pepper

2 (1-pound) Cornish game hens

▲ 1 cup reduced-sodium chicken broth

2 shallots, minced

1 tablespoon unsalted butter

1 Preheat oven to 450°F. Spray small roasting pan with olive oil nonstick spray.

2 Combine ¼ cup of preserves, the mustard, 1 teaspoon of rosemary, the salt, and pepper in small bowl. Gently loosen skin from breasts of hens; spread preserves mixture evenly under skin. Tie legs of each hen together with kitchen string and tuck wing tips under; place, breast side up, in prepared pan. Roast until instant-read thermometer inserted into thickest part of thigh (not touching bone) registers 165°F, about 1 hour.

3 Transfer hens to platter; cover loosely with foil to keep warm. Set roasting pan over two burners over high heat. Add broth, shallots, and remaining 1 tablespoon preserves and 2 teaspoons rosemary; bring to boil, scraping any browned bits from bottom of pan. Reduce heat and simmer until sauce is reduced to about ½ cup, about 5 minutes.

4 Remove roasting pan from heat; swirl in butter until melted. Split each hen in half. Transfer to platter and serve with sauce. Remove skin before eating.

PER SERVING (½ *hen and 2 tablespoons sauce*): 234 Cal, 7 g Total Fat, 3 g Sat Fat, 0 g Trans Fat, 105 mg Chol, 467 mg Sod, 20 g Carb, 11 g Sugar, 0 g Fib, 23 g Prot, 28 mg Calc.

stay on track

Make this dish company worthy by serving it with steamed slender green beans (haricots verts) and steamed baby potatoes tossed with chopped fresh parsley and finely grated lemon zest (5 ounces of cooked baby potatoes for each serving will increase the *PointsPlus* value by 3).

APRICOT AND MUSTARD–GLAZED
CORNISH HENS AND FARMERS'
MARKET TOMATO, EGGPLANT, AND
ZUCCHINI CASSEROLE, p.196

grilled vietnamese chicken thighs with mango relish

SERVES 6

PointsPlus value

PER SERVING

Finely grated zest and juice of 1 orange

▲ **1 jalapeño pepper, seeded and minced**

3 garlic cloves, minced

2 tablespoons reduced-sodium soy sauce

1 tablespoon Asian fish sauce

1 tablespoon packed brown sugar

6 (¼-pound) skinless boneless chicken thighs, trimmed

▲ **1 large mango, seeded and cut into small dice (about 1½ cups)**

▲ **⅓ cup chopped red onion**

¼ cup chopped fresh mint

3 tablespoons unseasoned rice vinegar

1 teaspoon granulated sugar

1 To make marinade, combine orange zest and juice, jalapeño, garlic, soy sauce, fish sauce, and brown sugar in large zip-close plastic bag; add chicken. Squeeze out air and seal bag; turn to coat chicken. Refrigerate, turning bag occasionally, at least 3 hours or up to overnight.

2 Spray grill rack with nonstick spray. Preheat grill to medium or prepare medium fire.

3 Remove chicken from marinade; discard marinade. Place chicken on grill rack and grill until instant-read thermometer inserted into thigh registers 165°F, about 8 minutes per side. Transfer chicken to platter and keep warm.

4 To make relish, stir together all remaining ingredients in serving bowl. Serve with chicken.

PER SERVING (*1 chicken thigh and about ¼ cup relish*): 217 Cal, 9 g Total Fat, 2 g Sat Fat, 0 g Trans Fat, 74 mg Chol, 481 mg Sod, 13 g Carb, 10 g Sugar, 1 g Fib, 21 g Prot, 31 mg Calc.

stay on track

Quinoa, considered a complete protein because it contains all the essential amino acids, tastes as good as it is good for you. Serve a bowl of it alongside these flavor-packed chicken thighs (½ cup cooked quinoa per serving will increase the *PointsPlus* value by *3*).

turkey cutlets with mesclun and passion fruit dressing

SERVES 4

▲ **¼ cup passion fruit pulp (about 4 passion fruits)**

2 tablespoons orange juice

1 tablespoon + 2 teaspoons extra-virgin olive oil

1 tablespoon lime juice

1 tablespoon honey

½ teaspoon salt

¼ + ⅛ teaspoon black pepper

Pinch cayenne

▲ **1 large egg white**

1 tablespoon water

▲ **⅓ cup yellow cornmeal**

3 tablespoons finely grated Parmesan cheese

▲ **4 (¼-pound) turkey breast cutlets**

▲ **6 ounces mesclun (about 8 lightly packed cups)**

1 To make dressing, whisk together passion fruit pulp, orange juice, 2 teaspoons of oil, the lime juice, honey, ¼ teaspoon of salt, ⅛ teaspoon of black pepper, and the cayenne in large bowl until blended; set aside.

2 Whisk together egg white and water in large shallow bowl. Mix together cornmeal, Parmesan, and remaining ¼ teaspoon salt and ¼ teaspoon pepper on sheet of wax paper.

3 Dip each cutlet into egg-white mixture, then coat with cornmeal mixture, pressing lightly so it adheres.

4 Heat remaining 1 tablespoon oil in large cast-iron or heavy nonstick skillet over medium-high heat. Add cutlets and cook until browned and cooked through, about 3 minutes per side.

5 Add mesclun to dressing; toss until coated evenly. Transfer 1 cutlet to each of 4 plates. Top evenly with salad.

PER SERVING *(1 turkey cutlet and about 2 cups salad):* 273 Cal, 6 g Total Fat, 1 g Sat Fat, 0 g Trans Fat, 45 mg Chol, 439 mg Sod, 24 g Carb, 8 g Sugar, 4 g Fib, 31 g Prot, 6 mg Calc.

JUST DELICIOUS TURKEY-CHUTNEY BURGERS

just delicious turkey-chutney burgers

SERVES 4

1 tablespoon canola oil

▲ 1 Granny Smith apple, peeled, cored, and coarsely grated

▲ 2 scallions, thinly sliced

▲ 1 celery stalk including leaves, finely chopped

▲ ¾ pound ground skinless turkey breast

¼ cup Major Grey's chutney, pieces finely chopped

¼ teaspoon salt

4 whole wheat hamburger buns, split and toasted

▲ 4 leaves Boston or frisée lettuce

▲ 8 thin slices red onion

1 Heat 2 teaspoons of oil in large nonstick skillet over medium heat. Add apple, scallions, and celery; cook, stirring, until celery is softened, about 5 minutes. Spread on plate and let cool completely.

2 Mix together turkey, cooled apple mixture, chutney, and salt in medium bowl. With damp hands, shape mixture into 4 (½-inch-thick) patties.

3 Add remaining 1 teaspoon oil to skillet and set over medium heat. Add patties and cook until instant-read thermometer inserted into side of burger registers 165°F for well done, about 5 minutes per side.

4 Place bottom of bun on each of 4 plates. Top each with 1 lettuce leaf, 2 slices of onion, and 1 burger. Cover with tops of buns.

PER SERVING (*1 garnished burger*): 315 cal, 7 g Fat, 1 g Sat Fat, 0 g Trans Fat, 34 mg Chol, 543 mg Sod, 41 g Carb, 17 g Sugar, 5 g Fib, 25 g Prot, 63 mg Calc.

for your info

The grated apple keeps the burgers moist while the chutney adds great flavor. The burgers can also be grilled. Just be sure to spray the grill rack with nonstick spray.

turkey, red bean, and chipotle pepper chili

SERVES 4

PER SERVING

1 tablespoon olive oil

▲ 1 onion, chopped

▲ 1 red bell pepper, chopped

4 garlic cloves, minced

▲ 1 pound ground skinless turkey breast

▲ 1 (28-ounce) can no-salt-added diced tomatoes

▲ 1 (15½-ounce) can no-salt-added red kidney beans, rinsed and drained

2–3 teaspoons chipotle chile powder

2 teaspoons ground cumin

1 teaspoon dried oregano

½ teaspoon salt

1 Heat oil in Dutch oven over medium heat. Add onion, bell pepper, and garlic; cook, stirring, until softened, about 5 minutes.

2 Add turkey to pot and cook, breaking it apart with wooden spoon, until no longer pink, about 3 minutes. Stir in all remaining ingredients and bring to boil. Reduce heat and simmer, covered, until vegetables are tender and flavors are blended, about 30 minutes.

PER SERVING (*about 1⅓ cups*): 317 Cal, 6 g Total Fat, 1 g Sat Fat, 0 g Trans Fat, 45 mg Chol, 416 mg Sod, 32 g Carb, 11 g Sugar, 13 g Fib, 37 g Prot, 109 mg Calc.

stay on track

Keep on plan and be even more satisfied by spooning the chili over hot cooked brown rice and topping each serving with a 2-tablespoon dollop of fat-free sour cream and a sprinkling of sliced scallion (½ cup of cooked brown rice per serving will increase the *PointsPlus* value by *3*).

grilled arctic char with cool sweet pea succotash

SERVES 6

- ▲ 1 (10-ounce) box frozen baby peas
- ▲ 1 (10-ounce) box frozen corn kernels
- ▲ 3 large plum or Kumato tomatoes (see tip page 63), seeded and cut into ½-inch dice
- ▲ 3 scallions, thinly sliced
- ▲ 6 radishes with green tops, radishes thinly sliced and tops coarsely chopped
- ¼ cup thinly sliced fresh basil
- 1 tablespoon extra-virgin olive oil
- 1 tablespoon sherry vinegar or cider vinegar
- 1 teaspoon salt
- ½ teaspoon black pepper
- ▲ 6 (¼-pound) arctic char fillets
- 6 lemon wedges

1 To make succotash, cook peas and corn according to package directions. Drain in colander, then hold under cold running water to stop cooking; drain again.

2 Stir together peas, corn, tomatoes, scallions, radishes and their tops, basil, oil, vinegar, ½ teaspoon of salt, and ¼ teaspoon of pepper in serving bowl. Let stand at room temperature up to 1 hour or refrigerate, covered, up to 4 hours.

3 Meanwhile, spray grill rack with nonstick spray. Preheat grill to medium-high or prepare medium-high fire.

4 Spray arctic char with olive oil nonstick spray. Sprinkle with remaining ½ teaspoon salt and ¼ teaspoon pepper. Place fillets on grill rack and grill until just opaque in center, about 3 minutes per side. Place 1 fillet on each of 6 plates and spoon succotash alongside. Serve with lemon wedges.

PER SERVING (*1 arctic char fillet and about ⅔ cup succotash*): 264 Cal, 10 g Total Fat, 2 g Sat Fat, 0 g Trans Fat, 55 mg Chol, 520 mg Sod, 18 g Carb, 5 g Sugar, 4 g Fib, 28 g Prot, 26 mg Calc.

new orleans halibut creole

SERVES 4

9
PointsPlus®
value

PER SERVING

- 2 teaspoons olive oil
- ▲ 2 red bell peppers, diced
- ▲ 1 onion, chopped
- ▲ 2 celery stalks, diced
- 3 large garlic cloves, minced
- 2 cups tomato juice
- 1 tablespoon mild cayenne pepper sauce, such as Frank's
- 2 teaspoons Worcestershire sauce
- ▲ 4 (5-ounce) halibut fillets
- ▲ 2 scallions, thinly sliced on diagonal
- ▲ 2 cups hot cooked brown rice

1 Heat oil in large nonstick skillet over medium heat. Add bell peppers, onion, celery, and garlic; cook, stirring, until onion is softened, about 5 minutes.

2 Add tomato juice, pepper sauce, and Worcestershire sauce to skillet; bring to boil. Reduce heat and simmer until vegetables are just softened, about 4 minutes.

3 Nestle halibut fillets into vegetables. Cook, covered, until fish is just opaque throughout, about 8 minutes. Sprinkle with scallions and serve with rice.

PER SERVING *(1 halibut fillet, 1 cup vegetables with sauce, and ½ cup rice):* 349 Cal, 7 g Total Fat, 1 g Sat Fat, 0 g Trans Fat, 45 mg Chol, 575 mg Sod, 37 g Carb, 9 g Sugar, 5 g Fib, 34 g Prot, 120 mg Calc.

stay on track

Add some healthful dark greens to your plate by serving a side of steamed broccoli florets alongside the fish and rice.

mediterranean-style roasted monkfish

SERVES 6

▲ **6 tomatoes, cut into thick wedges**

▲ **1 red onion, sliced**

6 pitted Kalamata olives, chopped

3 garlic cloves, minced

1 tablespoon olive oil

1½ teaspoons capers, drained

1 teaspoon dried oregano

1 teaspoon salt

½ teaspoon black pepper

▲ **6 (5-ounce) pieces monkfish fillet**

½ cup dry white wine

½ cup crumbled reduced-fat feta cheese

3 tablespoons coarsely chopped fresh flat-leaf parsley

Finely grated zest of 1 lemon

1 Preheat oven to 400°F. Spray medium roasting pan with olive oil nonstick spray.

2 Stir together tomatoes, onion, olives, garlic, oil, capers, oregano, ½ teaspoon of salt, and ¼ teaspoon of pepper in large bowl.

3 Arrange monkfish in prepared pan in single layer. Sprinkle with remaining ½ teaspoon salt and ¼ teaspoon pepper. Scatter tomato-onion mixture around fish; drizzle with wine. Roast until tomatoes are softened and fish is opaque in center, 25–30 minutes. Transfer fish and tomato mixture to platter.

4 Mix together feta, parsley, and lemon zest; sprinkle over vegetables.

PER SERVING (*1 piece monkfish and about ½ cup tomato mixture*)**:** 212 Cal, 7 g Total Fat, 2 g Sat Fat, 0 g Trans Fat, 39 mg Chol, 661 mg Sod, 9 g Carb, 4 g Sugar, 2 g Fib, 24 g Prot, 74 mg Calc.

moroccan salmon with tomato-saffron sauce

SERVES 4

5 PointsPlus value

PER SERVING

½ teaspoon saffron threads

¼ cup boiling water

▲ 2 scallions, thinly sliced

1 large garlic clove, minced

▲ 1 (14½-ounce) can diced tomatoes

½ teaspoon dried thyme

▲ 1 (1-pound) wild salmon or cod fillet, about 1 inch thick, cut into 4 equal pieces

½ teaspoon salt

¼ teaspoon black pepper

1 Crumble saffron into boiling water in cup. Let steep 10 minutes.

2 Combine scallions and garlic in large shallow glass bowl or casserole; spray with olive oil nonstick spray. Cover bowl with plastic wrap and poke a few holes in plastic. Microwave on High until fragrant, about 1 minute. Stir in tomatoes, saffron liquid, and thyme. Cover and microwave on High until flavors are blended, about 3 minutes.

3 Spray shallow microwavable dish large enough to hold fish in one layer with nonstick spray. Place salmon in dish; sprinkle with salt and pepper. Cover dish with wax paper and microwave on High until fish is just opaque in center, about 6 minutes. Spoon tomato sauce over fish. Remove skin before eating.

PER SERVING (*1 piece salmon and about* ⅓ *cup sauce*): 212 Cal, 8 g Total Fat, 1 g Sat Fat, 0 g Trans Fat, 72 mg Chol, 579 mg Sod, 6 g Carb, 3 g Sugar, 1 g Fib, 27 g Prot, 41 mg Calc.

stay on track

Serve the fish on a bed of whole wheat couscous (1 cup of cooked whole wheat couscous per serving will increase the *PointsPlus* value by *5*).

**MOROCCAN SALMON WITH
TOMATO-SAFFRON SAUCE**

crisp cod cakes with peach-basil relish

SERVES 4

- ▲ **2 large peaches, pitted and cut into ¼-inch dice (about 2 cups)**
- **¼ cup chopped fresh basil**
- **¼ cup chopped fresh mint**
- **2 shallots, finely chopped + 1 large shallot, halved**
- **2 teaspoons lime juice**
- **¾ teaspoon salt**
- **½ teaspoon black pepper**
- ▲ **1 pound cod fillet, skinned and cut into small pieces**
- **2 tablespoons chopped fresh parsley**
- **Finely grated zest of 1 lime**
- **2 teaspoons olive oil**

1 To make relish, stir together peaches, basil, mint, chopped shallots, lime juice, ¼ teaspoon of salt, and ¼ teaspoon of pepper in serving bowl.

2 To make cod cakes, combine cod, parsley, the halved shallot, lime zest, and remaining ½ teaspoon salt and ¼ teaspoon pepper in food processor; pulse until finely chopped. With damp hands, form cod mixture into 4 (½-inch-thick) patties.

3 Heat oil in large nonstick skillet over medium heat. Add patties and cook until browned and cooked through, about 6 minutes per side. Serve with relish.

PER SERVING (*1 cod cake and about ½ cup relish*): 152 Cal, 3 g Total Fat, 0 g Sat Fat, 0 g Trans Fat, 43 mg Chol, 501 mg Sod, 12 g Carb, 8 g Sugar, 2 g Fib, 19 g Prot, 39 mg Calc.

stay on track Keep the *PointsPlus* value low by serving a baby romaine salad sprinkled with red-wine vinegar and some Mediterranean herb–flavored fat-free feta cheese (1 ounce of fat-free feta per serving will increase the *PointsPlus* value by *1*).

tomato-smothered striped bass

SERVES 4

▲ **1 (14½-ounce) can crushed tomatoes**

3 tablespoons chopped fresh oregano

2 large garlic cloves, minced

¾ teaspoon salt

¼ teaspoon black pepper

Pinch cayenne

▲ **2 (½-pound) striped bass fillets, each cut crosswise in half**

2 ounces reduced-fat soft goat cheese, crumbled

▲ **2 cups hot cooked whole wheat orzo**

1 Preheat oven to 350°F.

2 Stir together tomatoes, 1 tablespoon of oregano, the garlic, ¼ teaspoon of salt, ⅛ teaspoon of black pepper, and the cayenne in medium bowl.

3 Spread half of tomato sauce in 7 x 11-inch baking dish. Arrange bass fillets on top of sauce in single layer. Sprinkle fish with remaining ½ teaspoon salt and ⅛ teaspoon black pepper. Spoon remaining tomato sauce evenly over fish and sprinkle with goat cheese. Cover dish tightly with foil.

4 Bake until fish is just opaque in center, about 20 minutes. Sprinkle fish with remaining 2 tablespoons oregano. Serve with orzo.

PER SERVING (*1 piece striped bass fillet with about ¼ cup sauce and ½ cup orzo*): 324 Cal, 6 g Total Fat, 1 g Sat Fat, 0 g Trans Fat, 96 mg Chol, 702 mg Sod, 38 g Carb, 1 g Sugar, 7 g Fib, 32 g Prot, 90 mg Calc.

POTATO CHIP–CRUSTED TROUT AND MIXED VEGETABLES
WITH ORANGE GREMOLATA, p. 181

potato chip-crusted trout

SERVES 4

8
PointsPlus value

PER SERVING

1 tablespoon fat-free mayonnaise

▲ 3 tablespoons plain fat-free yogurt

Pinch cayenne

▲ 4 (5-ounce) trout fillets

1½ cups baked curry-flavored potato chips

2 tablespoons finely chopped fresh parsley

1 Place oven rack in upper third of oven and preheat to 425°F. Line broiler rack with foil.

2 Stir together mayonnaise, yogurt, and cayenne in cup.

3 Place trout fillets, skin side down, on prepared broiler rack; brush mayonnaise mixture over fillets.

4 Put potato chips in large zip-close plastic bag. With rolling pin or meat mallet, coarsely crush chips. Sprinkle chips evenly over fish and lightly spray with nonstick spray. Roast until fish is just opaque in center, about 12 minutes.

5 Preheat broiler. Broil fish 5 inches from heat until potato chips are lightly browned, about 30 seconds. Sprinkle with parsley.

PER SERVING (*1 trout fillet*): 278 Cal, 12 g Total Fat, 2 g Sat Fat, 0 g Trans Fat, 81 mg Chol, 231 mg Sod, 11 g Carb, 2 g Sugar, 1 g Fib, 30 g Prot, 102 mg Calc.

stay on track

Add some fiber to your dinner by serving this fish along with green or brown lentils (½ cup of cooked lentils per serving will increase the *PointsPlus* value by *2*).

almost-blackened cast-iron skillet trout

SERVES 4

7 PointsPlus® value

PER SERVING

▲ **3 tablespoons cornmeal**

2 teaspoons smoked sweet paprika

2 teaspoons Old Bay seasoning

1 teaspoon black pepper

1 teaspoon packed brown sugar

1 teaspoon onion powder

1 teaspoon garlic powder

1 teaspoon dried thyme

½ teaspoon white pepper

▲ **1 large egg white**

▲ **4 (5-ounce) trout fillets**

1 tablespoon canola oil

Lemon wedges

1 On large sheet of wax paper, mix together cornmeal, paprika, Old Bay seasoning, black pepper, brown sugar, onion powder, garlic powder, thyme, and white pepper. With fork, beat egg white in large shallow bowl.

2 Dip trout fillets, one at a time, in egg white, then coat with spice mixture.

3 Heat large cast-iron or heavy nonstick skillet over medium-high heat; add oil. Add trout and cook until deeply browned and just opaque in center, about 3 minutes per side. Serve with lemon wedges.

PER SERVING (*1 trout fillet*): 280 Cal, 12 g Total Fat, 2 g Sat Fat, 0 g Trans Fat, 86 mg Chol, 138 mg Sod, 10 g Carb, 1 g Sugar, 1 g Fib, 31 g Prot, 74 mg Calc.

now try this

White pepper is made from peppercorns whose skin has been removed. It is milder than black pepper and is often used in dishes where black pepper specks are undesirable.

slow-cooker island-style shrimp and mussel stew

SERVES 6

PER SERVING

- ▲ **3 large red potatoes, scrubbed and cut into 1-inch chunks**
- ▲ **1 onion, chopped**
- ▲ **1 green bell pepper, coarsely chopped**
- **3 large garlic cloves, minced**
- ▲ **1 jalapeño pepper, seeded and minced**
- ▲ **3 (14½-ounce) cans diced tomatoes**
- **1 (8-ounce) bottle clam juice**
- **⅛ teaspoon cayenne or to taste**
- ▲ **1½ pounds medium shrimp, peeled and deveined**
- ▲ **2 dozen mussels, scrubbed and debearded**
- **⅓ cup shredded sweetened coconut, toasted**
- **⅓ cup chopped fresh cilantro**
- **Finely grated zest of ½ orange**
- **Hot pepper sauce for serving**

1 Combine potatoes, onion, bell pepper, garlic, jalapeño, tomatoes, and clam juice in 5- or 6-quart slow cooker. Sprinkle with cayenne. Cover and cook until potatoes are fork-tender, 4–5 hours on high or 8–10 hours on low.

2 Add shrimp to slow cooker. Cover and cook 10 minutes. Add mussels; cover and cook until shrimp are just opaque throughout and mussels open. Discard any mussels that do not open.

3 Turn off slow cooker and let stand 5 minutes. Ladle stew into 6 large shallow bowls and sprinkle evenly with coconut, cilantro, and orange zest. Serve with pepper sauce.

PER SERVING (*about 2 cups*): 329 Cal, 3 g Total Fat, 2 g Sat Fat, 0 g Trans Fat, 178 mg Chol, 854 mg Sod, 46 g Carb, 12 g Sugar, 6 g Fib, 28 g Prot, 112 mg Calc.

honey-glazed shrimp with gingery slaw

SERVES 6

- ▲ **4 cups shredded dark green cabbage**
- ▲ **3 carrots, cut into very thin matchsticks**
- **⅓ cup cider vinegar**
- **2 tablespoons canola oil**
- **1 tablespoon minced peeled fresh ginger**
- **¼ teaspoon red pepper flakes**
- ▲ **1½ pounds extra-large shrimp, peeled and deveined, tails left on if desired**
- **3 tablespoons honey**
- **½ teaspoon black pepper**
- **3 tablespoons finely chopped unsalted peanuts**
- **1 tablespoon chopped fresh mint**
- **1 tablespoon chopped fresh basil**
- **Lime wedges**

1 To make slaw, mix together cabbage, carrots, vinegar, oil, ginger, and pepper flakes in large bowl. Cover and refrigerate at least 2 hours or up to overnight.

2 Meanwhile, spray grill rack with nonstick spray. Preheat grill to medium-high or prepare medium-high fire.

3 Thread shrimp evenly onto 6 (12-inch) skewers, leaving small space between each shrimp.

4 Place skewers on grill rack and grill until shrimp are just opaque in center, about 3 minutes per side. Transfer skewers to platter and let cool slightly. Lightly brush shrimp with honey and sprinkle with black pepper and peanuts.

5 Mix together mint and basil in cup. Divide slaw among 6 plates and sprinkle with herb mixture. Place 1 shrimp skewer on top of each serving of slaw. Serve with lime wedges for squeezing over shrimp.

PER SERVING (*1 skewer and 1 cup slaw*): 213 Cal, 8 g Total Fat, 1 g Sat Fat, 0 g Trans Fat, 168 mg Chol, 224 mg Sod, 16 g Carb, 10 g Sugar, 2 g Fib, 20 g Prot, 71 mg Calc.

stay on track

Starting the meal off with a refreshing Spanish-style salad of fresh orange segments sprinkled with thinly sliced onion and sun-dried tomatoes (not packed in oil) will provide you with a generous dose of vitamin C and fiber.

HONEY-GLAZED SHRIMP WITH GINGERY SLAW

shrimp and penne arrabbiata

SERVES 4

PointsPlus®
value

PER SERVING

- ▲ **8 ounces whole wheat penne**
- **4 teaspoons olive oil**
- ▲ **1 pound large shrimp, peeled and deveined**
- **3 large garlic cloves, minced**
- ▲ **1 (14½-ounce) can fire-roasted crushed tomatoes**
- **3 tablespoons tomato paste**
- **½ teaspoon red pepper flakes**
- **¼ teaspoon salt**
- **8 large fresh basil leaves, chopped**
- **¼ cup finely grated Parmesan cheese**

1 Cook pasta according to package directions, omitting salt if desired. Drain and keep warm.

2 Heat 2 teaspoons of oil in large nonstick skillet over medium heat. Add shrimp, in batches, and cook until just opaque in center, about 2 minutes per side, transferring shrimp to plate as it is cooked. Keep warm.

3 Add remaining 2 teaspoons oil to skillet. Add garlic and cook, stirring, until fragrant, about 30 seconds. Stir in tomatoes, tomato paste, ¼ teaspoon of pepper flakes, and the salt; cook until slightly thickened, about 5 minutes. Taste sauce and add remaining ¼ teaspoon pepper flakes or to taste. Return shrimp to skillet along with pasta and basil; cook, stirring, just until heated through, about 2 minutes longer.

4 Divide shrimp-pasta mixture among 4 plates and sprinkle evenly with Parmesan.

PER SERVING (*about 1½ cups*): 384 Cal, 7 g Total Fat, 1 g Sat Fat, 0 g Trans Fat, 168 mg Chol, 702 mg Sod, 54 g Carb, 8 g Sugar, 7 g Fib, 27 g Prot, 66 mg Calc.

for your info

Arrabbiata, which means "angry" in Italian, is reflected by the generous amount of red pepper flakes in this classic Italian dish. Make it as "angry" as you like by altering the amount of pepper flakes.

tri-shellfish fra diavolo

SERVES 6

8 PointsPlus® value

PER SERVING

- ▲ **8 ounces whole wheat linguine**
- **1 tablespoon olive oil**
- ▲ **2 dozen mussels, scrubbed and debearded**
- ▲ **1 dozen littleneck clams, scrubbed**
- ▲ **1 pound large shrimp, peeled and deveined**
- ▲ **1 (28-ounce) can diced tomatoes**
- **½ cup dry white wine**
- **4 large garlic cloves, minced**
- **½ teaspoon red pepper flakes or to taste**

1 Cook pasta according to package directions, omitting salt if desired. Drain and keep warm.

2 Meanwhile, heat oil in large nonstick skillet over medium heat. Add mussels and clams; cook, covered, until they open, about 6 minutes for mussels and 8 minutes for clams. Transfer to large bowl as they open. Discard any clams and mussels that do not open.

3 Add shrimp to skillet and cook, stirring occasionally, just until opaque in center, about 3 minutes. Transfer to mussels and clams. Keep warm.

4 Add tomatoes, wine, garlic, and pepper flakes to skillet; bring to boil. Cook, stirring occasionally, until sauce is slightly thickened, 8–10 minutes.

5 Return seafood to skillet and gently reheat. Transfer pasta to large serving bowl. Spoon seafood and sauce over pasta.

PER SERVING (*about 2 cups*): 315 Cal, 5 g Total Fat, 1 g Sat Fat, 0 g Trans Fat, 134 mg Chol, 546 mg Sod, 38 g Carb, 6 g Sugar, 6 g Fib, 28 g Prot, 88 mg Calc.

tender littlenecks
in garlicky tomato sauce

SERVES 4

7 PointsPlus® value

PER SERVING

1 tablespoon olive oil

4 or 5 large garlic cloves, thinly sliced

▲ 1 (14½-ounce) can petite diced tomatoes

▲ 1 cup tomato puree

1 teaspoon dried oregano

⅛ teaspoon cayenne

▲ 5 dozen littleneck clams, scrubbed

3 tablespoons chopped fresh parsley

1 Heat oil in Dutch oven or large pot over medium heat. Add garlic and cook, stirring frequently, until golden, about 2 minutes.

2 Add tomatoes, tomato puree, oregano, and cayenne to pot; bring to boil. Reduce heat and simmer, stirring occasionally, until sauce is slightly thickened, about 5 minutes.

3 Add clams to pot and bring to boil. Reduce heat and simmer, covered, until clams open, about 7 minutes. Discard any clams that do not open. Divide clams and sauce among 4 bowls. Sprinkle with parsley.

PER SERVING (15 clams and about ⅔ cup sauce): 292 Cal, 6 g Total Fat, 1 g Sat Fat, 0 g Trans Fat, 95 mg Chol, 406 mg Sod, 18 g Carb, 4 g Sugar, 2 g Fib, 39 g Prot, 162 mg Calc.

corn, jalapeño, and cheese frittata

SERVES 4

PER SERVING

- ▲ **1 cup fat-free egg substitute**
- ▲ **2 large eggs**
- ▲ **1 cup frozen corn kernels, thawed**
- ▲ **2 scallions, sliced**
- ▲ **1 jalapeño pepper, seeded and minced**
- **2 tablespoons coarsely chopped fresh cilantro**
- ▲ **¼ cup fat-free milk**
- **1 teaspoon chili powder**
- **¼ teaspoon salt**
- **¼ teaspoon black pepper**
- **½ teaspoon canola oil**
- ▲ **12 grape tomatoes, halved**
- **¼ cup coarsely shredded reduced-fat Monterey Jack cheese**
- ▲ **½ cup fat-free salsa**

1 Whisk together egg substitute, eggs, corn, scallions, jalapeño, cilantro, milk, chili powder, salt, and black pepper in large bowl.

2 Coat medium nonstick skillet with oil and set over medium heat. Add egg mixture and sprinkle with tomatoes and Monterey Jack. Cook, covered, until eggs are set, about 12 minutes. Cut frittata into 4 wedges. Serve hot, warm, or at room temperature accompanied by salsa.

PER SERVING (*1 frittata wedge and 2 tablespoons salsa*): 165 Cal, 6 g Total Fat, 3 g Sat Fat, 0 g Trans Fat, 115 mg Chol, 659 mg Sod, 14 g Carb, 3 g Sugar, 1 g Fib, 14 g Prot, 257 mg Calc.

for your info

If you prefer your frittata lightly browned on top, after the eggs are set, put the frittata under a preheated broiler about 5 inches from the heat and broil until lightly browned, about 4 minutes.

baked eggs in smoky tomato sauce with feta and thyme

SERVES 4

5
PointsPlus
value
PER SERVING

2 teaspoons olive oil

▲ 1 small red onion, thinly sliced

1 garlic clove, minced

1 teaspoon chopped fresh thyme

½ teaspoon smoked paprika (see tip page 129)

▲ 1 (14½-ounce) can diced tomatoes

▲ 1 cup canned small white beans, rinsed and drained

▲ 4 large eggs

2 tablespoons crumbled reduced-fat feta cheese

1 tablespoon chopped fresh flat-leaf parsley

1 Preheat oven to 350°F.

2 Heat oil in medium skillet over medium heat. Add onion and cook, stirring, until softened, about 5 minutes. Add garlic, thyme, and paprika; cook, stirring constantly, until fragrant, about 30 seconds. Add tomatoes and bring to boil. Reduce heat and simmer, stirring frequently, until sauce is thickened, about 10 minutes. Stir in beans; divide among 4 (2-cup) baking dishes, or spoon into 7 x 9-inch baking dish or shallow 8-cup casserole.

3 Crack open eggs, one at a time, and place over tomato mixture in each individual baking dish or in large baking dishes, spacing evenly. Bake until egg whites are firm, but yolks are still soft, about 15 minutes for individual dishes or about 20 minutes for large dishes. Sprinkle with feta and parsley. Serve hot.

PER SERVING (¼ of tomato mixture and 1 egg): 181 Cal, 8 g Total Fat, 2 g Sat Fat, 0 g Trans Fat, 216 mg Chol, 624 mg Sod, 20 g Total Carb, 5 g Total Sugar, 5 g Fib, 12 g Prot, 93 mg Calc.

stay on track

Turn this brunch/lunch dish into a complete meal by serving it with your favorite mixed green salad and slices of toasted reduced-calorie whole wheat bread (1 slice of reduced-calorie whole wheat bread will increase the per-serving *PointsPlus* value by *1*).

BAKED EGGS IN SMOKY TOMATO SAUCE WITH FETA AND THYME

mexican tortilla and egg scramble

SERVES 4

3 PointsPlus® value

PER SERVING

2 (6-inch) corn tortillas

2 teaspoons canola oil

▲ ½ cup chopped red onion

▲ 2 plum tomatoes, seeded and chopped

▲ ½ small serrano pepper, seeded and minced

1 teaspoon ground cumin

¼ teaspoon salt

▲ 1 (16-ounce) container fat-free egg substitute

Fresh cilantro leaves for garnish

1 Lightly spray tortillas on both sides with nonstick spray; cut into thin strips.

2 Coat large nonstick skillet with ½ teaspoon of oil and set over medium heat. Add tortillas and cook, stirring, until crispy, about 5 minutes. Transfer to plate.

3 Add remaining 1½ teaspoons oil to skillet. Add onion and cook, stirring, until softened, about 5 minutes. Add tomatoes, serrano, cumin, and salt; cook, stirring constantly, about 30 seconds.

4 Scatter tortillas evenly over tomato mixture; pour egg substitute over. Cook, stirring, until eggs form large, soft curds, about 2 minutes. Sprinkle with cilantro.

PER SERVING (*about 1½ cups*): 111 Cal, 3 g Total Fat, 0 g Sat Fat, 0 g Trans Fat, 0 mg Chol, 345 mg Sod, 10 g Carb, 2 g Sugar, 1 g Fib, 11 g Prot, 52 mg Calc.

stay on track

Serve with a bowl of black beans mixed with brown rice (¼ cup canned black beans with ½ cup cooked brown rice per serving will increase the *PointsPlus* value by 4).

crispy quesadillas with black beans and cheese

SERVES 4

▲ **1 cup canned no-salt-added black beans, rinsed and drained**

▲ **4 scallions, thinly sliced**

½ **cup chopped fresh cilantro**

▲ **1 jalapeño pepper, seeded and minced**

8 (7-inch) whole wheat tortillas

½ **cup reduced-sodium Swiss cheese**

▲ ½ **cup fat-free tomato salsa**

1 Stir together beans, scallions, cilantro, and jalapeño in small bowl.

2 Spread bean mixture evenly over 4 tortillas. Sprinkle each with 2 tablespoons of Swiss cheese and 2 tablespoons of salsa. Cover with remaining 4 tortillas, pressing down lightly.

3 Set large nonstick skillet over medium heat. Spray top of 1 quesadilla with nonstick spray. Place, sprayed side down, in skillet and cook until tortilla is crisp and cheese begins to melt, about 2 minutes. Spray tortilla with nonstick spray; turn over and cook until browned in spots and crispy, about 2 minutes longer. Transfer to cutting board and cover loosely with foil to keep warm. Repeat with remaining 3 quesadillas. Cut each quesadilla into 4 wedges, making total of 16 wedges.

PER SERVING (*4 wedges*): 253 Cal, 9 g Total Fat, 2 g Sat Fat, 0 g Trans Fat, 10 mg Chol, 699 mg Sod, 40 g Carb, 1 g Sugar, 22 g Fib, 20 g Prot, 171 mg Calc.

**SOY AND HONEY–GLAZED
TOFU-VEGETABLE SKEWERS**

soy and honey–glazed tofu-vegetable skewers

SERVES 4

- ▲ **⅔ cup quinoa**
- **3 tablespoons reduced-sodium soy sauce**
- **2 tablespoons honey**
- **1 tablespoon lime juice**
- ▲ **1 (14-ounce) container firm or extra-firm tofu, drained and cut into 1-inch cubes**
- ▲ **1 yellow bell pepper, cut into 1-inch pieces**
- ▲ **1 green bell pepper, cut into 1-inch pieces**
- ▲ **1 small red onion, quartered and separated into layers**
- ▲ **8 large grape tomatoes**

1 Cook quinoa according to package directions, omitting salt if desired. Keep warm.

2 Stir together soy sauce, honey, and lime juice in cup; set aside.

3 Spray nonstick ridged grill pan with nonstick spray and set over medium-high heat. Alternately thread tofu, bell peppers, onion, and tomatoes onto 8 (12-inch) metal skewers; brush with soy sauce mixture.

4 Place skewers in pan and cook, turning, until tofu is browned and vegetables are softened, about 10 minutes. Serve over quinoa.

PER SERVING (*2 skewers and ½ cup quinoa*): 268 Cal, 7 g Total Fat, 1 g Sat Fat, 0 g Trans Fat, 0 mg Chol, 407 mg Sod, 39 g Carb, 13 g Sugar, 4 g Fib, 15 g Prot, 223 mg Calc.

stay on track

A dessert of sliced fresh peaches, sliced fresh apricots, and raspberries is a refreshing way to end this meal.

spicy two-bean vegetarian chili

SERVES 4

7 PointsPlus® value

PER SERVING

1 tablespoon olive oil

▲ 1 onion, chopped

▲ 1 green bell pepper, chopped

▲ 1 carrot, thinly sliced

▲ 1 or 2 jalapeño peppers, seeded and minced

3 large garlic cloves, minced

▲ 1 (28-ounce) can crushed tomatoes with added puree

▲ 1 (15½-ounce) can no-salt-added black beans, rinsed and drained

▲ 1 (15½-ounce) can no-salt-added red kidney beans, rinsed and drained

1 tablespoon chili powder

1 teaspoon ground cumin

1 teaspoon dried oregano

▲ 4 scallions, sliced

▲ ½ cup fat-free sour cream

1 Heat oil in Dutch oven over medium heat. Add onion, bell pepper, carrot, jalapeño, and garlic; cook, stirring, until onion is softened, about 5 minutes.

2 Stir tomatoes, black beans, kidney beans, chili powder, cumin, and oregano into pot; bring to boil. Reduce heat and simmer until chili is slightly thickened, about 20 minutes.

3 Divide chili among 4 bowls; top evenly with scallions and sour cream.

PER SERVING (*generous 1 cup chili and 2 tablespoons sour cream*): 330 Cal, 4 g Total Fat, 1 g Sat Fat, 0 g Trans Fat, 3 mg Chol, 416 mg Sod, 55 g Carb, 12 g Sugar, 17 g Fib, 18 g Prot, 249 mg Calc.

stay on track

Make this meatless chili even heartier by spooning it over soft polenta prepared from yellow cornmeal (½ cup polenta for each serving will increase the *PointsPlus* value by *3*).

slow-cooker white bean and spinach burritos

SERVES 8

PER SERVING

- ▲ 1 (14½-ounce) can no-salt-added diced tomatoes
- ▲ 2 (15½-ounce) cans no-salt-added small white beans, rinsed and drained
- ▲ 1 (8¾-ounce) can corn kernels, drained
- 3 tablespoons taco or Mexican seasoning
- 1 teaspoon ground cumin
- ▲ 2 cups lightly packed baby spinach
- 8 (7-inch) whole wheat tortillas, warmed
- ½ cup reduced-fat pepper Jack cheese
- ½ cup reduced-fat Cheddar cheese
- ▲ ½ cup fat-free tomato salsa
- ▲ ½ cup fat-free sour cream
- ½ cup lightly packed fresh cilantro leaves

1 Drain tomatoes, reserving all but ½ cup of liquid. Put tomatoes and reserved liquid in 5- or 6-quart slow cooker. Add beans, corn, taco seasoning, and cumin. Cover and cook until flavors are blended, 3–4 hours on high or 6–8 hours on low.

2 About 20 minutes before cooking time is up, stir in spinach. Coarsely mash bean mixture with potato masher.

3 Spoon ½ cup of bean mixture along center of each tortilla. Top with 1 tablespoon pepper Jack, 1 tablespoon Cheddar, 1 tablespoon salsa, 1 tablespoon sour cream, and 1 tablespoon cilantro. Roll up tortillas to enclose filling.

PER SERVING (1 *burrito*): 265 Cal, 8 g Total Fat, 3 g Sat Fat, 0 g Trans Fat, 15 mg Chol, 744 mg Sod, 38 g Carb, 5 g Sugar, 15 g Fib, 15 g Prot, 187 mg Calc.

cremini mushroom bolognese with pasta

SERVES 6

9 PointsPlus® value

PER SERVING

1 tablespoon olive oil

▲ 1 small onion, finely chopped

1 garlic clove, minced

▲ 1 small celery stalk including leaves, stalk finely diced and leaves chopped

▲ 1 small carrot, finely diced

½ teaspoon salt

⅛ teaspoon black pepper

▲ 2 cups finely chopped cremini mushroom caps (about 8 ounces mushrooms)

▲ 1 (14½-ounce) can petite diced tomatoes

▲ 1 tablespoon finely chopped dried mushrooms, such as porcini

▲ 1 pound whole wheat penne

¼ cup + 2 tablespoons finely grated Parmesan cheese

¼ cup reduced-fat (2%) milk, at room temperature

½ cup chopped fresh flat-leaf parsley

1 To make bolognese, heat oil in large nonstick skillet over medium heat. Add onion and cook, stirring, until softened, about 5 minutes. Stir in garlic and cook, stirring constantly, until fragrant, about 30 seconds. Stir in celery, carrot, salt, and pepper; cook, stirring frequently, until vegetables begin to soften, about 5 minutes.

2 Add cremini mushrooms to skillet. Increase heat to medium-high and cook, stirring frequently, until mushrooms release their liquid and it is almost evaporated, about 8 minutes. Add tomatoes and dried mushrooms; cook, stirring constantly, until most of liquid is evaporated, about 6 minutes longer.

3 Meanwhile, cook pasta according to package directions, omitting salt if desired. Drain and keep warm.

4 Add ¼ cup of Parmesan and the milk to bolognese; cook, stirring, until cheese is melted, about 1 minute.

5 Toss together bolognese, pasta, and parsley in serving bowl. Sprinkle with remaining 2 tablespoons Parmesan.

PER SERVING (1½ cups): 365 Cal, 6 g Total Fat, 1 g Sat Fat, 0 g Trans Fat, 5 mg Chol, 453 mg Sod, 64 g Carb, 7 g Sugar, 8 g Fib, 13 g Prot, 124 mg Calc.

stay on track

This mushroom-laden, flavor-packed pasta dish is sure to keep you well satisfied while staying on track.

thai rice noodles with tofu and cilantro

SERVES 6

PER SERVING

8 ounces rice stick noodles

⅓ cup ketchup

2 tablespoons Asian fish sauce

1 tablespoon packed brown sugar

4 teaspoons canola oil

▲ ½ cup fat-free egg substitute

3 large garlic cloves, minced

▲ ¾ pound reduced-fat extra-firm tofu, cut into ½-inch cubes

▲ 1 cup no-salt-added vegetable broth

▲ 4 scallions, thinly sliced on diagonal

½ cup coarsely chopped fresh cilantro

3 tablespoons finely chopped unsalted peanuts

Sriracha (hot chile sauce) for serving (see tip page 27)

Lime wedges for serving

1 Put noodles in large bowl and add enough hot water to cover. Let stand until softened, about 20 minutes; drain.

2 Meanwhile, stir together ketchup, fish sauce, and brown sugar in small bowl; set aside.

3 Heat 2 teaspoons of oil in large heavy nonstick skillet over medium-high heat. Add egg substitute and cook, stirring to form small curds, until set, about 1 minute. Transfer eggs to medium bowl.

4 Add remaining 2 teaspoons oil to skillet. Add garlic and cook, stirring constantly, until fragrant, about 30 seconds. Add tofu and cook, stirring occasionally, until heated through, about 3 minutes. Add to scrambled eggs.

5 Add noodles, broth, and ketchup mixture to skillet and cook, stirring, until noodles have absorbed almost all liquid, about 5 minutes. Return tofu-egg mixture to skillet along with scallions and cilantro; cook, stirring, about 30 seconds. Transfer noodle mixture to platter and sprinkle with peanuts. Serve with Sriracha and lime wedges.

PER SERVING (about 1 cup): 279 Cal, 7 g Total Fat, 1 g Sat Fat, 0 g Trans Fat, 0 mg Chol, 689 mg Sod, 40 g Carb, 6 g Sugar, 2 g Fib, 11 g Prot, 247 mg Calc.

chapter 5
sides from the garden

springtime asparagus with tarragon mimosa

SERVES 4

PER SERVING

▲ **1 (1-pound) bunch asparagus, trimmed and lower half of spears peeled**

2 tablespoons tarragon vinegar

1 tablespoon extra-virgin olive oil

1 shallot, minced

1 teaspoon Dijon mustard

½ teaspoon salt

¼ teaspoon black pepper

▲ **2 hard-cooked large eggs**

2 teaspoons chopped fresh tarragon + small sprigs for garnish

1 Prepare large bowl of ice water.

2 Put asparagus in large skillet and add enough cold water to cover; bring to boil. Reduce heat and simmer, covered, until asparagus are just tender, about 6 minutes. With tongs, transfer asparagus to ice water. When cool, transfer to double layer of paper towels and pat asparagus dry.

3 To make dressing, whisk together vinegar, oil, shallot, mustard, salt, and pepper in small bowl.

4 Peel and halve eggs; discard 1 yolk or reserve for another use. Finely chop whites. Press remaining yolk through coarse sieve set over small bowl. Gently stir together egg white, egg yolk, and chopped tarragon.

5 Toss asparagus with dressing in large shallow bowl; divide among 4 plates. Sprinkle evenly with egg-tarragon mixture. Garnish each serving with tarragon sprig.

PER SERVING (*about 5 asparagus spears and about 1 tablespoon mimosa*): 99 Cal, 6 g Total Fat, 1 g Sat Fat, 0 g Trans Fat, 106 mg Chol, 358 mg Sod, 6 g Carb, 3 g Sugar, 2 g Fib, 6 g Prot, 45 mg Calc.

for your info

Mimosa, a garnish that is comprised of finely chopped or grated hard-cooked egg white and yolk, is so named because of its color resemblance to the mimosa flower.

baked artichoke halves with lemony pecorino-romano stuffing

SERVES 6

4
PointsPlus
value

PER SERVING

1 large lemon

▲ 3 large artichokes

1½ cups fresh whole wheat bread crumbs (about 3 slices bread)

3 tablespoons finely grated pecorino-romano cheese

¼ cup chopped fresh flat-leaf parsley

3 large garlic cloves, minced

2 teaspoons extra-virgin olive oil

▲ ¼ cup reduced-sodium chicken broth or water

1 Fill large nonreactive pot with water and bring to boil.

2 Finely grate zest from lemon and set aside. Halve lemon and squeeze juice into large bowl of cold water; drop in lemon halves. Working with one artichoke at a time, snap off and discard dark green outer leaves. Cut off stem. With small knife, peel tough skin from stem. Slice off and discard 1 inch from top of artichoke. Drop trimmed artichoke and stem into lemon water to prevent browning. Repeat with remaining artichokes.

3 With slotted spoon, transfer artichokes and lemon halves to boiling water; return to boil. Reduce heat and simmer, covered, until small knife inserted into base of artichoke and stem goes in easily, about 20 minutes; drain. Rinse under cold running water. Drain. Cut each artichoke in half. With small spoon, scoop out and discard fuzzy choke and violet-tipped leaves. Finely chop stems.

4 Preheat oven to 400°F. Spray 9 x 13-inch baking dish with olive oil nonstick spray.

5 Spread bread crumbs in shallow baking pan and toast, shaking pan occasionally, until golden, about 5 minutes. Stir together bread crumbs, pecorino-romano, parsley, chopped artichoke stems, reserved lemon zest, garlic, and oil in medium bowl, adding a little water if mixture seems dry. Divide filling among artichoke cavities. Spray with nonstick spray.

6 Place stuffed artichokes in prepared baking dish. Pour broth around artichokes. Cover dish loosely with foil and bake 15 minutes. Remove foil and bake until artichokes are heated through and topping is lightly browned, 15–20 minutes longer.

PER SERVING (*1 stuffed artichoke half*): 161 Cal, 4 g Total Fat, 1 g Sat Fat, 0 g Trans Fat, 4 mg Chol, 431 mg Sod, 23 g Carb, 4 g Sugar, 4 g Fib, 7 g Prot, 137 mg Calc.

**BAKED ARTICHOKE HALVES WITH
LEMONY PECORINO-ROMANO STUFFING**

chilled asparagus with sour cream–dill sauce

SERVES 4 • 20 MINUTES

2 PointsPlus® value

PER SERVING

**1 (1-pound) bunch asparagus, trimmed**

¼ cup water

¼ cup reduced-fat mayonnaise

¼ cup reduced-fat sour cream

Finely grated zest of 1 lemon

1 tablespoon lemon juice

2 tablespoons snipped fresh dill + sprigs for garnish

½ teaspoon honey

1 Prepare large bowl of ice water.

2 Place asparagus and water in large microwavable dish, tips facing toward center. Cover with plastic wrap and vent one corner. Microwave on High until crisp-tender, about 3 minutes. With tongs, transfer asparagus to ice water to cool. Transfer to double layer of paper towels and pat dry. Arrange asparagus on platter.

3 To make sauce, stir together all remaining ingredients in small bowl. Spoon over asparagus. Garnish with dill sprigs.

PER SERVING *(about 5 asparagus spears and 2½ tablespoons sauce)*: 81 Cal, 4 g Total Fat, 2 g Sat Fat, 0 g Trans Fat, 5 mg Chol, 144 mg Sod, 9 g Carb, 4 g Sugar, 3 g Fib, 4 g Prot, 54 mg Calc.

stay on track

For only a few *PointsPlus* value, you get a spectacular asparagus dish. Turn it into a complete meal by serving lemon-garlic shrimp and baked sweet potatoes alongside (4 ounces of cooked large shrimp and 1 medium baked sweet potato for each serving will increase the *PointsPlus* value by *6*).

parmesan and black pepper green beans

SERVES 4 • 20 MINUTES

▲ **1 pound green beans and/or wax beans, trimmed**

1 tablespoon extra-virgin olive oil

½ teaspoon dried thyme

½ teaspoon salt

¼ teaspoon black pepper

¼ cup coarsely grated Parmesan cheese

1 Fill large nonstick skillet with ¾ inch of water and bring to boil. Add green beans and cook, covered, just until tender, 5–7 minutes. Drain.

2 Reduce heat to medium. Add oil, thyme, salt, and pepper to beans in skillet; toss until mixed well. Cook, tossing, until heated through, about 1 minute. Transfer beans to serving bowl and sprinkle with Parmesan.

PER SERVING (*1 cup*): 87 Cal, 5 g Total Fat, 1 g Sat Fat, 0 g Trans Fat, 4 mg Chol, 374 mg Sod, 8 g Carb, 2 g Sugar, 4 g Fib, 4 g Prot, 101 mg Calc.

green beans and zucchini with spiced honey almonds

SERVES 4

PER SERVING

¼ cup whole blanched almonds

1¼ teaspoons sugar

¼ teaspoon ground cinnamon

¼ teaspoon salt

Pinch cayenne

½ teaspoon honey

▲ ¾ pound green beans, trimmed and halved

▲ 1 zucchini (about ¾ pound), cut into ¼-inch-thick matchsticks

2 tablespoons snipped fresh chives

2 teaspoons extra-virgin olive oil

⅛ teaspoon black pepper

1 Preheat oven to 350°F. Spray small baking pan with olive oil nonstick spray.

2 Put almonds in prepared pan and bake, shaking pan occasionally, until lightly toasted, 10–12 minutes.

3 Meanwhile, to make spice mixture, mix together sugar, cinnamon, ⅛ teaspoon of salt, and the cayenne in cup. Drizzle honey over warm almonds; with rubber spatula mix until coated evenly. Add spice mixture, stirring vigorously until coated.

4 Spread nuts in pan and bake until glazed looking, stirring once or twice and watching to avoid overbrowning, about 8 minutes. Let cool in pan 5 minutes, then with wide spatula, scrape nuts onto plate. Let cool completely, then chop.

5 Bring 1 inch of water to boil in large saucepan. Set steamer basket in saucepan and add green beans. Reduce heat to medium and cook, covered, 4 minutes. Place zucchini on top of beans; steam until vegetables are just tender, 3–5 minutes longer. Remove steamer basket with vegetables from saucepan; with tongs, transfer vegetables to serving bowl.

6 Sprinkle chives over vegetables; drizzle with oil and sprinkle with remaining ⅛ teaspoon salt and the pepper. Toss until mixed well; sprinkle with spiced almonds.

PER SERVING (*1 cup*): 114 Cal, 7 g Total Fat, 1 g Sat Fat, 0 g Trans Fat, 0 mg Chol, 303 mg Sod, 12 g Carb, 4 g Sugar, 5 g Fib, 4 g Prot, 64 mg Calc.

mixed vegetables with orange gremolata

SERVES 6

2 PointsPlus® value

PER SERVING

3 tablespoons chopped fresh parsley

2 tablespoons chopped fresh tarragon

Finely grated zest of 1 small orange

1 tablespoon orange juice

1 garlic clove, minced

1 tablespoon extra-virgin olive oil

1 large shallot, chopped (about ⅓ cup)

▲ ½ pound slender green beans (haricots verts), trimmed

▲ 1 yellow squash, cut into ¼-inch-thick matchsticks

▲ 2 large carrots, cut into ¼-inch-thick matchsticks

▲ 1 red bell pepper, cut into ¼-inch-thick matchsticks

¾ teaspoon salt

¼ teaspoon black pepper

▲ ¼ cup reduced-sodium chicken or vegetable broth

1 To make gremolata, mix together parsley, tarragon, orange zest and juice, garlic, and 1 teaspoon of oil in small bowl. Cover bowl with plastic wrap and set aside. Can be prepared up to several hours ahead and refrigerated.

2 Heat remaining 2 teaspoons oil in large nonstick skillet over medium heat. Add shallot and cook, stirring, until softened, about 2 minutes. Add green beans, squash, carrots, bell pepper, salt, and black pepper; toss until mixed well. Cook, stirring occasionally, 2 minutes.

3 Add broth to skillet and bring to boil. Reduce heat and simmer, covered, stirring occasionally, until vegetables are crisp-tender, about 5 minutes.

4 Add half of gremolata to skillet and toss until mixed. Spoon vegetables into serving dish and sprinkle with remaining gremolata.

PER SERVING (¾ cup): 64 Cal, 3 g Total Fat, 0 g Sat Fat, 0 g Trans Fat, 0 mg Chol, 316 mg Sod, 9 g Carb, 3 g Sugar, 3 g Fib, 2 g Prot, 41 mg Calc.

for your info

Gremolata, which is almost always sprinkled over osso buco (braised veal shanks), is also excellent over cooked whole baby potatoes, grilled or broiled chicken breasts, or grilled or broiled fish. If you like, use lemon or lime zest instead of the orange zest or a combination.

GRILLED BELL PEPPERS
WITH HALOUMI CHEESE
AND SLIVERED BASIL

grilled bell peppers with haloumi cheese and slivered basil

SERVES 6

3 PointsPlus® value

PER SERVING

▲ **2 red bell peppers**

▲ **2 yellow bell peppers**

6 (scant ½-inch) slices haloumi cheese, cut in half on diagonal

¼ cup pitted Kalamata olives, chopped

2 tablespoons thinly sliced fresh basil

1 tablespoon balsamic vinegar

1 tablespoon water

1 teaspoon extra-virgin olive oil

¼ teaspoon salt

¼ teaspoon red pepper flakes

1 Spray grill rack with nonstick spray. Preheat grill to medium or prepare medium fire.

2 Cut each bell pepper lengthwise into 6 pieces; remove seeds. Place peppers on grill rack and grill until tender and lightly charred, about 6 minutes per side. Transfer to platter.

3 Spray haloumi with nonstick spray. Place cheese on grill rack and grill until well marked, about 2 minutes per side. Arrange on platter; scatter olives and basil over bell peppers and cheese.

4 To make dressing, whisk together vinegar, water, oil, salt, and pepper flakes in small bowl. Drizzle dressing over bell peppers and cheese.

PER SERVING (*about 1 cup*): 110 Cal, 7 g Total Fat, 3 g Sat Fat, 0 g Trans Fat, 10 mg Chol, 395 mg Sod, 8 g Carb, 4 g Sugar, 1 g Fib, 4 g Prot, 140 mg Calc.

now try this

Haloumi (hah-LOO-mee) cheese is a very mild sheep's milk cheese that is popular in Turkey and Cyprus. What makes this cheese special is that it holds its shape when grilled, just softening slightly. It can be found in supermarkets, specialty food stores, and Middle Eastern markets.

stir-fried broccoli with scallion and bacon

SERVES 4

PER SERVING

2 teaspoons canola oil

2 slices Canadian bacon, halved and thinly sliced

▲ 4 cups broccoli florets

¼ cup Shao Hsing rice wine

▲ 2 scallions, cut into 1½-inch lengths

1 tablespoon finely grated peeled fresh ginger

1 tablespoon reduced-sodium soy sauce

2 teaspoons packed brown sugar

2 teaspoons toasted sesame seeds

1 Heat wok over medium-high heat until drop of water sizzles in pan. Add oil and swirl to coat pan. Add Canadian bacon and stir-fry until lightly browned, about 2 minutes. Transfer to plate.

2 Add broccoli to wok and stir-fry 2 minutes. Add wine and cook, covered, until broccoli is crisp-tender, about 3 minutes. Add scallions and ginger; stir-fry until fragrant, about 30 seconds. Add soy sauce and brown sugar; stir-fry 30 seconds longer.

3 Return Canadian bacon to wok and stir fry until heated through, about 1 minute. Spoon broccoli mixture into serving bowl and sprinkle with sesame seeds.

PER SERVING (*1 cup*): 120 Cal, 6 g Total Fat, 1 g Sat Fat, 0 g Trans Fat, 7 mg Chol, 340 mg Sod, 9 g Carb, 3 g Sugar, 3 g Fib, 6 g Prot, 48 mg Calc.

tuscan-style broccoli with garlic chips

SERVES 4

 **1 bunch broccoli, tops cut into 2-inch florets and stems thinly sliced**

2 teaspoons extra-virgin olive oil

3 large garlic cloves, thinly sliced

¼ teaspoon salt

¼ teaspoon red pepper flakes

⅛ teaspoon black pepper

¼ cup finely grated Parmesan cheese

1 Bring 1 inch of water to boil in large saucepan. Add broccoli and cook, covered, until just tender, about 5 minutes. Drain.

2 Heat oil in large nonstick skillet over medium heat. Add garlic and cook, stirring, until golden, about 3 minutes; transfer to cup.

3 Add broccoli, salt, pepper flakes, and black pepper to skillet; cook, stirring, until heated through, about 2 minutes. Transfer broccoli to serving bowl and sprinkle with garlic chips and Parmesan.

PER SERVING (*about 1¼ cups*): 97 Cal, 4 g Total Fat, 1 g Sat Fat, 0 g Trans Fat, 4 mg Chol, 272 mg Sod, 11 g Carb, 3 g Sugar, 4 g Fib, 6 g Prot, 132 mg Calc.

stay on track

To turn this garlicky, cheesy broccoli into a hearty meatless main dish while getting a healthy dose of vitamins and fiber, serve it over brown rice (1 cup cooked brown rice per serving will increase the *PointsPlus* value by **5**).

balsamic vinegar–glazed brussels sprouts

SERVES 4

1 tablespoon olive oil

▲ 1 pound Brussels sprouts, trimmed and halved if large

¼ teaspoon salt

⅛ teaspoon black pepper

▲ ½ cup reduced-sodium chicken or vegetable broth

4 large shallots, thinly sliced (about ¾ cup)

1 tablespoon sugar

¼ cup good-quality balsamic vinegar

1 Heat oil in large heavy nonstick skillet over medium-high heat. Add Brussels sprouts and sprinkle with salt and pepper. Cook, stirring often, until Brussels sprouts are browned, about 5 minutes.

2 Add broth to skillet and bring to boil. Reduce heat and simmer, covered, until Brussels sprouts are crisp-tender, about 8 minutes.

3 Add shallots and sugar to skillet; cook over medium heat, stirring, until shallots are wilted, about 3 minutes. Add vinegar and cook, stirring, until liquid is reduced and syrupy and Brussels sprouts are glazed, about 2 minutes longer.

PER SERVING (*generous ½ cup*): 127 Cal, 4 g Total Fat, 1 g Sat Fat, 0 g Trans Fat, 0 mg Chol, 190 mg Sod, 21 g Carb, 8 g Sugar, 4 g Fib, 5 g Prot, 65 mg Calc.

braised winter cabbage with apple and tangerine

SERVES 4

1 tablespoon olive oil

▲ 1 small red onion, sliced (about 1 cup)

1 tablespoon packed brown sugar

½ teaspoon ground cinnamon

¼ teaspoon ground ginger

¼ teaspoon salt

⅛ teaspoon black pepper

Pinch ground allspice

▲ 4 cups shredded red cabbage (about half medium head)

½ cup water

▲ 2 Granny Smith apples, halved, cored, and sliced

3 tablespoons dry red wine or red grape juice

2 teaspoons finely grated tangerine or orange zest

2 tablespoons tangerine or orange juice

1 Heat oil in large heavy saucepan over medium heat. Add onion and cook, stirring, until softened, about 5 minutes. Stir in brown sugar, cinnamon, ginger, salt, pepper, and allspice.

2 Add cabbage and water to saucepan; bring to boil. Cook, stirring, until cabbage is slightly wilted, about 2 minutes. Add apples, wine, and tangerine zest and juice; bring to boil. Reduce heat to low and cook, covered, stirring occasionally, until cabbage is very tender, about 30 minutes.

PER SERVING (¾ cup): 132 Cal, 4 g Total Fat, 1 g Sat Fat, 0 g Trans Fat, 0 mg Chol, 171 mg Sod, 25 g Carb, 17 g Sugar, 4 g Fib, 2 g Prot, 51 mg Calc.

for your info

Braising is a cooking method in which the food is first browned in oil, then slowly cooked in a small amount of liquid over low heat until very tender. Food can be braised on top of a stove or in the oven. This cooking method makes our cabbage dish meltingly tender, deeply flavored, and easy to prepare.

ROASTED CAULIFLOWER "STEAKS" WITH
BROWN BUTTER RYE CRUMBS

roasted cauliflower "steaks" with brown butter rye crumbs

SERVES 4

▲ **1 head cauliflower (see tip page 191)**

¼ teaspoon salt

¼ teaspoon black pepper

2 tablespoons unsalted butter

2 teaspoons lemon juice

¾ cup fresh rye bread crumbs (about 1½ slices bread)

¼ cup chopped fresh flat-leaf parsley, snipped fresh chives, or a combination

2 teaspoons finely grated lemon zest

1 teaspoon tiny (nonpareil) capers, drained, rinsed, and chopped

Fresh chives, cut into 2-inch lengths

1 Preheat oven to 425°F. Spray large heavy rimmed baking sheet with olive oil nonstick spray.

2 Place cauliflower, core side down, on cutting board. Starting in middle of head, with large knife, cut 4 (¾-inch-thick) slices. Trim stems, if necessary. Cut remaining cauliflower into florets and reserve for another use.

3 Lightly spray slices of cauliflower on one side with nonstick spray and sprinkle with ⅛ teaspoon of salt and ⅛ teaspoon of pepper. Place cauliflower, seasoned side down, on prepared baking sheet. Spray cauliflower with nonstick spray and sprinkle with remaining ⅛ teaspoon salt and ⅛ teaspoon pepper.

4 Roast cauliflower until golden on bottom, about 15 minutes. With wide metal spatula, carefully turn cauliflower over and roast until tender and browned, about 15 minutes longer. Arrange on platter; keep warm.

5 Meanwhile, melt butter in small nonstick skillet over medium heat. Cook, shaking skillet occasionally, until butter is browned, about 2 minutes. Add lemon juice, then stir in bread crumbs, parsley, lemon zest, and capers. Cook, stirring, until crumbs are crisp and golden, about 2 minutes. Spoon crumb mixture evenly over cauliflower. Sprinkle with chives.

PER SERVING (*1 cauliflower "steak" and 2 tablespoons crumb mixture*): 137 Cal, 6 g Total Fat, 4 g Sat Fat, 0 g Trans Fat, 15 mg Chol, 312 mg Sod, 18 g Carb, 6 g Sugar, 6 g Fib, 5 g Prot, 64 mg Calc.

stay on track

Love omega-3 packed wild salmon? Serve fillets topped with a cherry tomato, red onion, and cilantro relish along with the cauliflower. A grilled or broiled 5½-ounce wild salmon fillet for each serving will increase the *PointsPlus* value by 7.

carrot puree with horseradish and honey

SERVES 4

2 teaspoons unsalted butter

2 garlic cloves, thinly sliced

▲ 1½ pounds carrots, cut into ½-inch slices (scant 4 cups)

▲ ½ cup reduced-sodium chicken or vegetable broth

▲ ⅓ cup fat-free half-and-half

1½ tablespoons prepared white horseradish

1 tablespoon honey

¼ teaspoon salt

¼ teaspoon coarsely ground black pepper

1 Melt butter in medium heavy saucepan over medium heat. Add garlic and cook, stirring often, until golden and butter is lightly browned, about 3 minutes.

2 Add carrots and broth to saucepan; bring to boil. Reduce heat and simmer, covered, stirring occasionally, until carrots are tender, about 10 minutes. Drain, reserving 2 tablespoons cooking liquid.

3 Transfer carrots and 1 tablespoon of reserved cooking liquid to food processor. Pulse until carrots are coarsely pureed, occasionally stopping machine to scrape down side of bowl and adding remaining 1 tablespoon cooking liquid if puree is too thick. Add half-and-half, horseradish, honey, salt, and ⅛ teaspoon of pepper, pulsing until combined. Transfer carrot mixture to serving bowl; sprinkle with remaining ⅛ teaspoon pepper.

PER SERVING (*generous ½ cup*): 129 Cal, 3 g Total Fat, 1 g Sat Fat, 0 g Trans Fat, 5 mg Chol, 332 mg Sod, 24 g Carb, 14 g Sugar, 5 g Fib, 3 g Prot, 96 mg Calc.

curried cauliflower

SERVES 6

1 tablespoon olive oil

▲ 1 onion, chopped

3 large garlic cloves, minced

2 teaspoons ground cumin

2 teaspoons curry powder

¾ teaspoon salt

⅛ teaspoon cayenne

▲ 1 head orange, purple, green, or white cauliflower, cut into small florets

1½ cups water

2 teaspoons sherry vinegar

1 Heat oil in Dutch oven over medium heat. Add onion and cook, stirring, until softened, about 5 minutes. Add garlic, cumin, curry powder, salt, and cayenne; cook, stirring frequently, until fragrant, about 30 seconds.

2 Add cauliflower to pot and stir until coated with spice mixture. Stir in water and bring to boil. Reduce heat and simmer, covered, stirring occasionally, until cauliflower is tender, 8–10 minutes. With slotted spoon, transfer cauliflower to serving bowl. Keep warm.

3 Bring cooking liquid to boil; boil until reduced to ½ cup, about 4 minutes. Stir in vinegar. Spoon over cauliflower.

PER SERVING (*1 cup*): 70 Cal, 3 g Total Fat, 0 g Sat Fat, 0 g Trans Fat, 0 mg Chol, 338 mg Sod, 11 g Carb, 5 g Sugar, 5 g Fib, 3 g Prot, 51 mg Calc.

now try this

Even though **white cauliflower** is the variety most commonly used, there are other types available: orange cauliflower gets its color from the presence of a high level of vitamin A, while the deep purple variety gets its glorious color from anthocyanins, an antioxidant. The green variety, also called broccoflower, comes in both a round and a spiky version, known as Romanesco.

mexican corn on the cob

SERVES 4

 **4 ears of corn, unhusked**

¼ cup fat-free mayonnaise

1–2 teaspoons chipotle chile powder

⅓ cup finely shredded Cotija (see tip page 61) or crumbled feta cheese

Lime wedges

1 Preheat grill to medium or prepare medium fire.

2 Meanwhile, soak corn in cold water to cover at least 10 minutes or up to 30 minutes. Drain and pat dry with paper towels. Place unhusked corn on grill rack and grill, turning, until husks are lightly charred all over, about 10 minutes.

3 Remove corn from grill. When cool enough to handle, remove husks and silk, leaving stalk attached. Return corn to grill and grill until nicely charred all over and tender, about 10 minutes longer. Place corn on platter.

4 Stir together mayonnaise and chile powder in cup. Brush over top of corn and sprinkle evenly with cotija. Serve with lime wedges for squeezing over corn.

PER SERVING (*1 ear of corn*): 128 Cal, 4 g Total Fat, 2 g Sat Fat, 0 g Trans Fat, 13 mg Chol, 292 mg Sod, 21 g Carb, 5 g Sugar, 3 g Fib, 5 g Prot, 68 mg Calc.

stay on track

This classic Mexican street snack is a little higher in *PointsPlus* value than some other side dishes, but with a healthy dose of fiber from the corn and some protein from the cheese, you are sure to keep hunger at bay while staying on plan.

MEXICAN CORN ON THE COB

basil, corn, and cheddar spoon bread

SERVES 6

5
PointsPlus
value

PER SERVING

- ▲ **2 cups fat-free milk**
- **1 tablespoon olive oil**
- **½ teaspoon salt**
- ▲ **½ cup cornmeal, preferably stone-ground**
- ▲ **1 (10-ounce) box frozen corn kernels, thawed**
- ▲ **½ cup coarsely shredded fat-free sharp or extra-sharp Cheddar cheese**
- **¼ cup chopped fresh basil**
- **¼ teaspoon black pepper**
- ▲ **2 large egg yolks**
- ▲ **4 large egg whites**
- **¼ teaspoon cream of tartar**

1 Preheat oven to 375°F. Spray 8-inch square or round baking dish or casserole with nonstick spray.

2 Combine milk, oil, and salt in large saucepan; bring to boil over medium-high heat. Very slowly whisk in cornmeal. Reduce heat to medium-low and cook, stirring constantly with wooden spoon, until mixture is thickened and smooth, about 5 minutes. Remove saucepan from heat; stir in corn, Cheddar, basil, and pepper until cheese is melted.

3 Spoon cornmeal mixture into large bowl and let cool slightly. Stir in egg yolks, one at a time, until blended.

4 With electric mixer on high speed, beat egg whites until foamy; add cream of tartar and beat until soft peaks form when beaters are lifted. Stir one-fourth of beaten egg whites into cornmeal mixture to lighten. With rubber spatula, gently fold in remaining egg whites just until no longer visible. Gently scrape mixture into prepared baking dish and smooth top. Bake until puffed and cooked through, about 30 minutes.

PER SERVING (*generous ¾ cup*): 194 Cal, 4 g Total Fat, 1 g Sat Fat, 0 g Trans Fat, 73 mg Chol, 334 mg Sod, 27 g Carb, 4 g Sugar, 1 g Fib, 12 g Prot, 197 mg Calc.

for your info

Regular cornmeal is made by grinding dried corn between metal rollers. The germ and hull is then removed, giving the meal its fine texture. Stone-ground cornmeal is made by grinding corn between millstones, which leaves the germ and hull intact making it highly nutritious. This process also lends the cornmeal its characteristic gritty texture. When purchasing, look for the words "stone-ground whole corn" on the label.

scalloped tomatoes with lots of herbs

SERVES 4

1½ cups fresh whole grain or whole wheat bread crumbs (about 3 slices bread)

¼ cup chopped fresh flat-leaf parsley

1 large shallot, minced (¼ cup)

3 tablespoons snipped fresh chives

1 tablespoon chopped fresh thyme

1 tablespoon chopped fresh oregano

2 large garlic cloves, minced

1 tablespoon extra-virgin olive oil

1½ teaspoons sugar

½ teaspoon salt

¼ teaspoon black pepper

▲ **2 pounds small tomatoes, cut into ½-inch slices**

1 Preheat oven to 400°F. Spray 9-inch deep-dish pie plate or 6-cup shallow casserole with olive oil nonstick spray.

2 Stir together bread crumbs, parsley, shallot, chives, thyme, oregano, and garlic in small bowl. Add oil, stirring until crumbs are just moistened. Scatter ¾ cup of crumb mixture in bottom of prepared pie plate. With back of spoon, press crumbs to form even layer. Bake until crust is golden brown, 8–10 minutes. Transfer pie plate to wire rack and let cool.

3 Meanwhile, mix together sugar, salt, and pepper in cup. Arrange half of tomatoes over crust in concentric circles, overlapping slices. Sprinkle with half of sugar-salt mixture and half of remaining crumb mixture. Arrange remaining tomatoes on top; sprinkle with remaining sugar-salt mixture and top with remaining crumb mixture. (Pie plate will be very full.)

4 Bake until tomatoes are softened and juices are bubbling, 40–45 minutes. Let cool slightly before serving.

PER SERVING (¾ cup): 138 Cal, 5 g Total Fat, 1 g Sat Fat, 0 g Trans Fat, 0 mg Chol, 387 mg Sod, 21 g Carb, 9 g Sugar, 5 g Fib, 5 g Prot, 63 mg Calc.

farmers' market tomato, eggplant, and zucchini casserole

SERVES 4

PER SERVING

▲ 2 teaspoons olive oil

▲ 1 small eggplant (about ¾ pound), cut into 1-inch chunks

▲ ½ red onion, chopped (about 1 cup)

3 large garlic cloves, minced

½ teaspoon salt

▲ ¾ pound small tomatoes, preferably heirloom, cut into ¼-inch slices

▲ 1 small zucchini, cut into ¼-inch rounds

▲ 1 small yellow squash, cut into ¼-inch rounds

¼ cup chopped fresh parsley

2 tablespoons chopped fresh basil

1 tablespoon chopped fresh oregano

⅛ teaspoon black pepper

2 teaspoons extra-virgin olive oil

2 tablespoons finely grated Asiago or Parmesan cheese

1 Preheat oven to 400°F. Spray shallow 5-cup casserole or 9-inch deep-dish pie plate with olive oil nonstick spray.

2 Heat ½ teaspoon of oil in large cast-iron or heavy nonstick skillet over medium-high heat. Add eggplant, onion, garlic, and ¼ teaspoon of salt; cook, stirring often, until eggplant is very tender and browned in spots, about 10 minutes, reducing heat, if needed. Transfer to prepared casserole.

3 Arrange tomatoes, zucchini, and yellow squash alternately on top of eggplant in rows, overlapping slices. Mix together parsley, basil, oregano, pepper, and remaining ¼ teaspoon salt in small bowl; sprinkle over vegetables; lightly spray with nonstick spray.

4 Bake until vegetables are juicy, browned along edges, and very tender, 25–30 minutes. Sprinkle evenly with Asiago and bake until melted, about 2 minutes longer. Serve hot, warm, or at room temperature.

PER SERVING (*1 cup*): 106 Cal, 6 g Total Fat, 1 g Sat Fat, 0 g Trans Fat, 2 mg Chol, 343 mg Sod, 12 g Carb, 6 g Sugar, 5 g Fib, 4 g Prot, 71 mg Calc.

caramelized vegetable ratatouille

SERVES 4

3 PointsPlus® value

PER SERVING

▲ 1 (1-pound) eggplant, unpeeled and cut into ½-inch dice

▲ ¾ pound zucchini, cut into ½-inch dice

▲ 1 large red bell pepper, cut into ½-inch pieces

▲ 1 onion, chopped

1 tablespoon extra-virgin olive oil

4 large garlic cloves, minced

▲ 1 (14½-ounce) can diced tomatoes

¾ teaspoon dried oregano or thyme

8 large fresh basil leaves, torn

¼ teaspoon salt

¼ teaspoon black pepper

⅛ teaspoon cayenne

1 Place oven racks in upper and lower thirds of oven and preheat to 450°F. Spray two rimmed baking sheets with olive oil nonstick spray.

2 Combine eggplant, zucchini, bell pepper, and onion in large bowl. Lightly spray with nonstick spray and toss until coated evenly. Divide vegetables between prepared baking sheets and spread to form even layer. Roast, tossing occasionally, until vegetables are tender and browned in spots, about 30 minutes, rotating baking sheets from top to bottom halfway through roasting. Transfer vegetables to large bowl. Keep warm.

3 Meanwhile, heat oil in Dutch oven over medium heat. Add garlic and cook, stirring, until fragrant, about 1 minute. Stir in tomatoes and oregano; cook, stirring occasionally, until mixture begins to thicken, about 8 minutes. Stir in eggplant mixture, basil, salt, black pepper, and cayenne; cook until flavors are blended, about 5 minutes. Serve hot, warm, or at room temperature.

PER SERVING (¾ *cup*): 124 Cal, 4 g Total Fat, 1 g Sat Fat, 0 g Trans Fat, 0 mg Chol, 390 mg Sod, 21 g Carb, 11 g Sugar, 7 g Fib, 4 g Prot, 63 mg Calc.

stay on track

Turn this ratatouille into a tasty lunch or snack while having some good-for-you whole grains. Serve it with slices of toasted and quartered reduced-calorie whole wheat bread (1 slice of reduced-calorie whole wheat bread per serving will increase the *PointsPlus* value by *1*).

baked spinach-cheese gratin

SERVES 4

2 teaspoons unsalted butter

▲ 1 Vidalia onion, coarsely chopped (2 cups)

2 garlic cloves, minced

½ teaspoon dried oregano

⅛ teaspoon ground nutmeg

⅛ teaspoon salt

⅛ teaspoon black pepper

▲ 1 (16-ounce) bag frozen chopped spinach, thawed and gently squeezed dry (don't remove all moisture)

2 tablespoons all-purpose flour

▲ 1 cup reduced-sodium chicken or vegetable broth

¼ cup coarsely shredded Swiss or Jarlsberg cheese

3 tablespoons whole wheat panko (Japanese bread crumbs)

1 tablespoon finely grated Parmesan cheese

1 Preheat oven to 375°F. Spray 9-inch pie plate or shallow 4-cup casserole with nonstick spray.

2 Melt butter in large nonstick skillet over medium heat. Add onion and garlic; cook, stirring, until onion is softened, about 5 minutes. Stir in oregano, nutmeg, salt, and pepper. Add spinach and cook, tossing, until heated through, about 1 minute. Sprinkle with flour; reduce heat and cook, stirring, 2 minutes. Add broth, a little at a time, stirring until bubbly. Let cook 1 minute. Scrape spinach mixture into prepared pie plate.

3 Mix together Swiss cheese, panko, and Parmesan in small bowl. Sprinkle evenly over spinach. Bake until spinach mixture is heated through and topping is lightly browned, about 20 minutes. Let stand a few minutes before serving.

PER SERVING (*about ¾ cup*): 143 Cal, 5 g Total Fat, 3 g Sat Fat, 0 g Trans Fat, 12 mg Chol, 361 mg Sod, 17 g Carb, 4 g Sugar, 3 g Fib, 8 g Prot, 157 mg Calc.

for your info

Make this dish even tastier by preparing it with one pound of fresh organic baby spinach from a farmers' market, if possible. Drop the spinach into a pot of salted boiling water and cook just until wilted, about 2 minutes. Drain in a colander and rinse under cool running water. Squeeze out the excess liquid and chop, then use in the recipe as directed.

charred summer squash with parmesan and mint

SERVES 4

-  **12 ounces small squash, such as zucchini, yellow, or patty pan, cut lengthwise in half or in quarters if thick**
- **2 teaspoons olive oil**
- **¼ teaspoon black pepper**
- **¼ teaspoon salt**
- **1½ tablespoons lemon juice**
- **⅓ cup coarsely grated Parmesan cheese**
- **¼ cup small mint leaves**
- **Lemon wedges**

1 Heat large cast-iron or other heavy skillet over high heat until very hot, about 5 minutes.

2 Meanwhile, put squash in large bowl and toss with oil and pepper until coated evenly.

3 Arrange half of squash in single layer and cook, turning once, until tender and charred in spots, about 7 minutes. Transfer to platter and keep warm. Repeat with remaining squash.

4 Sprinkle squash evenly with salt and drizzle with lemon juice. Sprinkle with Parmesan and mint; serve with lemon wedges.

PER SERVING (¾ cup): 69 Cal, 4 g Total Fat, 2 g Sat Fat, 0 g Trans Fat, 5 mg Chol, 266 mg Sod, 5 g Carb, 2 g Sugar, 1 g Fib, 4 g Prot, 106 mg Calc.

rainbow slaw

SERVES 4

2 PointsPlus® value PER SERVING

▲ **3 cups shredded red cabbage**

▲ **½ cup matchstick-cut carrot**

▲ **1 yellow bell pepper, thinly sliced**

▲ **2 scallions, thinly sliced**

¼ cup coarsely chopped fresh parsley

¼ cup reduced-fat sour cream

▲ **3 tablespoons fat-free half-and-half**

2 tablespoons red-wine vinegar

1½ tablespoons light agave nectar (see tip page 109) or 1 tablespoon honey

½ teaspoon salt

¼ teaspoon black pepper

1 Toss together cabbage, carrot, bell pepper, scallions, and parsley in serving bowl.

2 To make dressing, whisk together all remaining ingredients in small bowl. Add dressing to cabbage mixture and toss until coated evenly. Serve or cover and refrigerate up to 4 hours. Toss again just before serving.

PER SERVING (*1 cup*): 94 Cal, 2 g Total Fat, 1 g Sat Fat, 0 g Trans Fat, 5 mg Chol, 339 mg Sod, 16 g Carb, 10 g Sugar, 3 g Fib, 3 g Prot, 82 mg Calc.

For even more vegetable goodness, serve the slaw on a bed of baby arugula or other favorite greens.

fiery cabbage salad with lime-sriracha dressing

SERVES 6

2 PointsPlus® value

PER SERVING

▲ **5 cups finely shredded Napa cabbage**

▲ **4 mini cucumbers, quartered lengthwise and sliced**

▲ **1 green bell pepper, cut into ¼-inch dice**

⅓ cup chopped fresh cilantro

▲ **½ small red onion, finely chopped**

2 tablespoons lime juice

2 tablespoons finely grated peeled fresh ginger

1 tablespoon + ½ teaspoon Asian fish sauce

1 tablespoon packed brown sugar

2 teaspoons Asian (dark) sesame oil

1–2 teaspoons Sriracha (hot chile sauce; see tip page 27)

1 Toss together cabbage, cucumbers, bell pepper, cilantro, and onion in serving bowl.

2 To make dressing, whisk together all remaining ingredients in small bowl. Pour dressing over cabbage mixture and toss until coated well. Serve or cover and refrigerate up to overnight. For the best flavor, let the salad stand out at room temperature for about 1 hour before serving.

PER SERVING (*1 generous cup*): 53 Cal, 2 g Total Fat, 0 g Sat Fat, 0 g Trans Fat, 0 mg Chol, 402 mg Sod, 9 g Carb, 4 g Sugar, 2 g Fib, 2 g Prot, 43 mg Calc.

two-cabbage slaw with gingery peanut dressing

SERVES 4

- ▲ 2½ cups finely shredded red cabbage
- ▲ 2½ cups finely shredded green cabbage
- ▲ 1 orange or yellow bell pepper, thinly sliced
- ▲ 1 Asian pear or Granny Smith apple, unpeeled, cored and cut into matchsticks
- ▲ ½ small red onion, very thinly sliced
- ¼ cup chopped fresh parsley
- 3 tablespoons cider vinegar
- 3 tablespoons reduced-fat creamy peanut butter
- 2 tablespoons reduced-sodium soy sauce
- 1 tablespoon coarsely chopped peeled fresh ginger
- 1 tablespoon honey

1 Toss together red cabbage, green cabbage, bell pepper, Asian pear, onion, and parsley in serving bowl.

2 To make dressing, combine all remaining ingredients in blender or mini food processor; puree. Drizzle dressing over cabbage mixture and toss until coated evenly. Serve or cover and refrigerate up to 4 hours.

PER SERVING (1¼ cups): 152 Cal, 5 g Total Fat, 1 g Sat Fat, 0 g Trans Fat, 0 mg Chol, 384 mg Sod, 25 g Carb, 11 g Sugar, 5 g Fib, 5 g Prot, 56 mg Calc.

paris bistro–style celery root rémoulade

SERVES 4

▲ 1 (1½-pound) celery root, peeled,

¼ cup fat-free mayonnaise

2 tablespoons crème fraîche or sour cream

1 tablespoon finely chopped fresh parsley

2 teaspoons lemon juice

1 teaspoon Dijon mustard

1 teaspoon tiny (nonpareil) capers, drained and finely chopped

¼ teaspoon black pepper

1 In food processor fitted with shredding disk or with vegetable slicer fitted with julienne blade, coarsely shred enough celery root to equal 5 lightly packed cups.

2 To make dressing, whisk together all remaining ingredients in large bowl. Add celery root and toss until coated evenly. Cover and refrigerate at least 1 hour or up to 1 day to allow flavors to blend. Serve at cool room temperature for the best flavor.

PER SERVING (¾ cup): 103 Cal, 2 g Total Fat, 1 g Sat Fat, 0 g Trans Fat, 6 mg Chol, 351 mg Sod, 19 g Carb, 5 g Sugar, 3 g Fib, 3 g Prot, 81 mg Calc.

now try this

Crème fraîche, French for "fresh cream," is heavy cream that has been combined with buttermilk and set aside until it thickens and develops a slightly sour, nutty flavor and velvety texture. To make your own, combine 1 cup heavy cream (not ultra-pasteurized) with 2 tablespoons buttermilk in a covered glass jar. Let stand, undisturbed, at room temperature until thickened, about 24 hours, then refrigerate up to seven days. Crème fraîche can be found in most supermarkets and in specialty food stores.

FENNEL-APPLE SALAD WITH
ORANGE-MINT DRESSING

fennel-apple salad with orange-mint dressing

SERVES 4 • 20 MINUTES

▲ **1 large fennel bulb, halved lengthwise and very thinly sliced**

▲ **2 Golden Delicious or other sweet apples, halved, cored, and thinly sliced**

▲ **8 French breakfast or red radishes, thinly sliced**

3 tablespoons lightly packed fresh mint leaves, torn if desired

▲ **⅓ cup plain fat-free Greek yogurt**

2 teaspoons finely grated orange zest

3 tablespoons orange juice

1 teaspoon ground cumin

½ teaspoon ground coriander

½ teaspoon salt

¼ teaspoon black pepper

1 Toss together fennel, apples, radishes, and mint in serving bowl.

2 To make dressing, whisk together all remaining ingredients in small bowl. Spoon dressing over fennel mixture and toss until coated evenly. Serve or cover and refrigerate up to 4 hours.

PER SERVING (*about 1 cup*): 86 Cal, 0 g Total Fat, 0 g Sat Fat, 0 g Trans Fat, 0 mg Chol, 334 mg Sod, 20 g Carb, 10 g Sugar, 5 g Fib, 3 g Prot, 60 mg Calc.

now try this

French breakfast radishes, *les radis petit déjeuner* in French, are long, thin red radishes that are white at their root end. They are milder than red radishes and are often enjoyed with a dab of softened butter or in a radish and butter sandwich.

chapter 6

sides from the ground and grain

indian-spiced potato cakes with yogurt-mint chutney

SERVES 4

▲ **1 pound Yukon Gold potatoes, peeled and cut into 1-inch chunks**

3 large garlic cloves, peeled

▲ **¼ cup plain fat-free Greek yogurt**

½ cup chopped fresh cilantro

¼ cup chopped fresh mint

▲ **2 scallions, finely chopped**

▲ **1 Thai red chile, seeded and minced**

1 teaspoon ground cumin

½ teaspoon honey or light agave nectar (see tip page 109)

⅓ cup plain dried whole wheat bread crumbs

1 tablespoon grated peeled fresh ginger

¾ teaspoon garam masala

¼ teaspoon salt

2 teaspoons canola oil

1 Combine potatoes and garlic in large saucepan and add enough cold water to cover; bring to boil. Reduce heat and simmer, covered, until potatoes are tender, about 15 minutes; drain. Let cool slightly.

2 Meanwhile, to make chutney, stir together yogurt, ¼ cup of cilantro, the mint, scallions, chile, ½ teaspoon of cumin, and the honey in serving bowl.

3 With potato masher, coarsely mash potatoes and garlic. Add bread crumbs, remaining ¼ cup cilantro, the ginger, garam masala, remaining ½ teaspoon cumin, and the salt; stir until mixed well. With damp hands, shape mixture into 4 (½-inch-thick) patties.

4 Heat oil in large nonstick skillet over medium heat. Add patties and cook until browned and crispy, about 5 minutes per side. Serve with chutney.

PER SERVING (*1 potato cake and 2 tablespoons chutney*): 174 Cal, 3 g Fat, 0 g Sat Fat, 0 g Trans Fat, 0 mg Chol, 270 mg Sod, 31 g Carb, 4 g Sugar, 3 g Fib, 5 g Prot, 62 mg Calc.

now try this

Garam masala, Urdu for "hot spice," is a blend of up to 12 spices that is used in north Indian cooking. The blend often includes cardamom, cinnamon, cloves, coriander, cumin, and pepper. Because the spices are roasted before they are mixed together, garam masala does not have to be cooked to bring out its flavor, Instead, it can be added to food at the end of cooking or sprinkled over finished dishes.

crisp and tender mustard-roasted potatoes

SERVES 4

PER SERVING

- ▲ 3 (5-ounce) Yukon Gold potatoes, scrubbed
- ▲ 1 red onion
- ⅓ cup whole grain Dijon mustard, such as Maille
- 2 teaspoons extra-virgin olive oil
- 2 teaspoons chopped fresh rosemary + 2 teaspoons rosemary needles
- ¼ teaspoon black pepper

1 Preheat oven to 400°F. Spray medium rimmed baking sheet with olive oil nonstick spray.

2 Halve potatoes and cut each half lengthwise into 4 wedges. Halve onion through stem end and cut each half into 6 wedges.

3 Toss together potatoes, onion, mustard, oil, chopped rosemary, and pepper in large bowl. Spread potato mixture to form single layer in prepared pan, placing potatoes cut side down. Roast until bottoms of potatoes are deep golden and crisp, about 30 minutes. Turn potatoes over and roast until crisp on second side and tender, about 20 minutes longer. Sprinkle with rosemary needles.

PER SERVING (6 potato wedges and 3 onion wedges): 131 Cal, 4 g Fat, 0 g Sat Fat, 0 g Trans Fat, 0 mg Chol, 411 mg Sod, 25 g Carb, 5 g Sugar, 4 g Fib, 4 g Prot, 38 mg Calc.

stay on track

These hearty, full-flavored mustard-laced potatoes make a tasty side dish for grilled extra-lean burgers (5% fat) served with romaine lettuce and sliced tomato. A 3-ounce grilled or broiled extra-lean burger per serving will increase the *PointsPlus* value by *3*.

packet-grilled potatoes with smoked sea salt

SERVES 6

▲ **1½ pounds red, white, and/or blue baby (1-inch) potatoes, scrubbed (see tip page 216)**

⅓ cup chopped mixed fresh herbs, such as thyme, rosemary, and oregano

1 tablespoon garlic oil or basil oil

¾ teaspoon smoked or plain sea salt

¼ teaspoon black pepper

1 Spray grill rack with nonstick spray. Preheat grill to medium or prepare medium fire.

2 Toss together potatoes, herbs, oil, salt, and pepper in large bowl until coated evenly. Stack 2 (18 x 20-inch) sheets of heavy-duty foil to form double layer. Spray foil with nonstick spray. Place potato mixture in center of foil. To close packet, bring two opposite long sides of foil up to meet in center; fold edges over twice making ½-inch-wide folds to seal tightly. Double-fold the two open sides to seal tightly.

3 Place packet on grill rack and grill, turning occasionally, until potatoes are fork-tender, about 20 minutes. Open packet carefully (to avoid steam) and transfer to serving bowl.

PER SERVING (*about 1 cup*): 102 Cal, 3 g Total Fat, 0 g Sat Fat, 0 g Trans Fat, 0 mg Chol, 113 mg Sod, 19 g Carb, 1 g Sugar, 2 g Fib, 2 g Prot, 20 mg Calc.

POTATO-CARAWAY ROSTI WITH
BACON AND CHIVES

potato-caraway rosti with bacon and chives

SERVES 4

PER SERVING

- **3 slices turkey bacon, chopped**
- ▲ **2 russet potatoes (1½ pounds), scrubbed, coarsely grated, and squeezed dry**
- ▲ **1 small onion, coarsely grated**
- **1 tablespoon snipped fresh chives + snipped chives for sprinkling**
- **½ teaspoon caraway seeds**
- **¼ teaspoon salt**
- **¼ teaspoon black pepper**
- **2 teaspoons canola oil**
- ▲ **¼ cup fat-free sour cream**

1 Cook bacon in medium nonstick skillet over medium heat until browned, about 5 minutes. Transfer to paper towels to drain. Wipe skillet clean.

2 Stir together potatoes, onion, bacon, the 1 tablespoon of chives, the caraway seeds, salt, and pepper in large bowl until mixed well.

3 Add 1 teaspoon of oil to skillet and set over medium heat. Add potato mixture, spreading it and pressing down to form even layer. Cook, without stirring, until potatoes are browned on bottom, about 10 minutes.

4 Invert large plate on top of potato cake and carefully turn skillet over. Add remaining 1 teaspoon oil to skillet. Slide potato cake back into skillet and cook, without stirring, until browned on bottom, about 6 minutes. Cut rosti into 4 wedges and sprinkle with chives. Serve with sour cream.

PER SERVING (*1 wedge with 1 tablespoon sour cream*): 196 Cal, 5 g Fat, 1 g Sat Fat, 0 g Trans Fat, 12 mg Chol, 410 mg Sod, 35 g Carb, 4 g Sugar, 4 g Fib, 8 g Prot, 51 mg Calc.

for your info

Rosti is the Swiss word for "crisp and golden." This dish, similar to hash browns, has long been enjoyed by the farmers in Bern, Switzerland, where it originated.

olive oil–crushed potatoes with lemon salt

SERVES 4

▲ **1 pound baby (1-inch) potatoes, scrubbed and halved**

Finely grated zest of 1 lemon

¾ teaspoon kosher salt

1 tablespoon chopped fresh thyme

2 teaspoons extra-virgin olive oil

¾ teaspoon smoked paprika (see tip page 129)

1 Put potatoes in large saucepan and add enough cold water to cover by 1 inch; bring to boil. Reduce heat and simmer, covered, until potatoes are tender, about 15 minutes; drain.

2 Meanwhile, mix together lemon zest and salt in cup.

3 With fork, lightly crush potatoes. Stir in thyme, oil, and paprika. Transfer potatoes to serving bowl; sprinkle with lemon salt.

PER SERVING (½ *cup*): 102 Cal, 3 g Fat, 0 g Sat Fat, 0 g Trans Fat, 0 mg Chol, 391 mg Sod, 19 g Carb, 1 g Sugar, 2 g Fib, 2 g Prot, 17 mg Calc.

stay on track

Got leftovers? Start your day off with a hearty, satisfying serving of these potatoes warmed in the microwave and topped with a poached large egg for an additional *PointsPlus* value of *2*.

bacon and cucumber–studded german potato salad

SERVES 6

▲ 1¼ pounds waxy potatoes

2 slices turkey bacon, chopped

2 teaspoons olive oil

▲ 1 small onion, chopped

▲ ½ cup reduced-sodium chicken broth

3 tablespoons cider vinegar

▲ ½ cup diced mini or English (seedless) cucumber

2 tablespoons Dijon mustard

2 tablespoons chopped fresh flat-leaf parsley

¼ teaspoon salt

¼ teaspoon black pepper

1 Put potatoes in medium saucepan and add enough cold water to cover by 1 inch; bring to boil. Reduce heat and simmer, covered, until potatoes are fork-tender, about 15 minutes; drain. When cool enough to handle, peel potatoes and cut into thick slices. Transfer to serving bowl; keep warm.

2 Cook bacon in medium nonstick skillet over medium heat until crisp, about 5 minutes. Transfer to paper towels to drain.

3 Add oil and onion to skillet; cook, stirring until onion is softened, about 5 minutes. Add onion to bacon; keep warm.

4 Add broth and vinegar to skillet; bring to boil. Pour over warm potatoes and gently toss. Cover and let stand, stirring occasionally, 20 minutes. Pour off any liquid that is not absorbed. Add cucumber, bacon, onion, mustard, parsley, salt, and pepper to potatoes; toss until mixed well. Serve warm or at room temperature.

PER SERVING (*scant 1 cup*): 141 Cal, 3 g Total Fat, 1 g Sat Fat, 0 g Trans Fat, 5 mg Chol, 335 mg Sod, 25 g Carb, 1 g Sugar, 2 g Fib, 6 g Prot, 15 mg Calc.

rustic potato-fontina galette

SERVES 4

▲ ½ pound Yukon Gold potatoes, scrubbed and cut into ⅛-inch slices

▲ ½ pound purple or red potatoes, scrubbed and cut into ⅛-inch slices

¼ cup coarsely shredded fontina or Jarlsberg cheese

2 large shallots, finely chopped

1 tablespoon chopped fresh parsley

2 teaspoons finely chopped fresh rosemary

2 large garlic cloves, minced

½ teaspoon salt

¼ teaspoon black pepper

1 Preheat oven to 425°F. Separate ring and bottom of 9-inch springform pan. Spray side of pan with olive oil nonstick spray. Place 11-inch sheet of parchment paper on small baking sheet and lightly spray with nonstick spray. Place pan ring on parchment.

2 Toss together Yukon Gold and purple potatoes in large bowl until mixed. Toss together fontina, shallots, parsley, rosemary, garlic, salt, and pepper in small bowl until mixed well.

3 Arrange half of potatoes inside pan ring in concentric circles, overlapping slices slightly. Sprinkle evenly with half of cheese mixture. Layer with remaining potatoes and sprinkle evenly with remaining cheese mixture. Carefully release and lift off pan ring. Lightly spray potatoes with nonstick spray.

4 Roast potatoes until tender and nicely browned along edges, about 45 minutes. Slide galette onto serving plate. Cut into 4 wedges.

PER SERVING (*1 wedge*): 117 Cal, 2 g Fat, 1 g Sat Fat, 0 g Trans Fat, 8 mg Chol, 346 mg Sod, 23 g Carb, 3 g Sugar, 2 g Fib, 5 g Prot, 64 mg Calc.

now try this

There are several varieties of purple-fleshed, purple-skinned potatoes. **Blue Peruvians** date back thousands of years. More recent varieties include Adirondack Blues, developed in 2003, and Purple Majesty, which are the most vibrant-colored variety. Purple potatoes owe their color to the presence of anthocyanins, a flavonoid that is also present in berries and pomegranates.

RUSTIC POTATO-FONTINA GALETTE

wheat berry blt salad

SERVES 6

PER SERVING

- ▲ **1 cup wheat berries, rinsed**
- **3 cups water**
- **4 slices Canadian bacon**
- ▲ **1 small sweet onion, thinly sliced**
- ▲ **2 cups lightly packed bite-size pieces romaine lettuce**
- ▲ **3 large plum tomatoes, cut into thin wedges**
- **¼ cup chopped fresh parsley**
- **6 large fresh basil leaves, thinly sliced**
- **2–3 tablespoons white balsamic or cider vinegar**
- **1 tablespoon olive oil**
- **¼ teaspoon salt**
- **¼ teaspoon black pepper**

1 Combine wheat berries and water in medium saucepan and set over medium-high heat; bring to boil. Reduce heat and simmer, covered, until wheat berries are softened, about 1 hour. Drain and transfer to large bowl; let cool.

2 Meanwhile, spray large nonstick skillet with nonstick spray and set over medium heat. Add Canadian bacon and cook until lightly browned, about 4 minutes per side. Transfer to plate.

3 Add onion to skillet and cook, stirring occasionally, until it begins to brown, about 6 minutes. Add to wheat berries.

4 Chop Canadian bacon and add to wheat berry mixture along with all remaining ingredients. Toss until mixed well. Serve at room temperature.

PER SERVING (*about 1 cup*): 179 Cal, 4 g Total Fat, 1 g Sat Fat, 0 g Trans Fat, 9 mg Chol, 354 mg Sod, 26 g Carb, 3 g Sugar, 4 g Fib, 9 g Prot, 34 mg Calc.

toasted barley with corn, tomatoes, and baby spinach

SERVES 4

5
PointsPlus®
value
PER SERVING

▲ ½ cup pearl barley

▲ 2 cups reduced-sodium vegetable broth

▲ 2 cups lightly packed baby spinach

▲ 1 large poblano pepper

2 teaspoons olive oil

▲ 1 small red onion, chopped

2 garlic cloves, minced

▲ 1 cup grape tomatoes, halved

▲ 1 cup drained canned corn

½ cup coarsely chopped fresh cilantro

¼ teaspoon salt

¼ teaspoon black pepper

Large pinch cayenne or to taste

1 Put barley in large heavy saucepan and cook over medium heat, stirring, until toasted, about 10 minutes. Add broth and bring to boil. Reduce heat and simmer, covered, until barley is tender, about 35 minutes, stirring in spinach after barley has cooked 25 minutes. Drain off any excess liquid; transfer barley mixture to serving bowl.

2 Meanwhile, put poblano over gas flame or under preheated broiler and cook until blackened on all sides, about 10 minutes. Transfer to zip-close plastic bag; seal bag and let steam 10 minutes. When cool enough to handle, peel, seed, and dice pepper. Add to barley mixture.

3 Heat oil in medium nonstick skillet over medium heat. Add onion and cook, stirring, until lightly browned, about 8 minutes. Add garlic and cook, stirring, until fragrant, about 1 minute longer.

4 Add onion-garlic mixture and all remaining ingredients to barley mixture. Toss until mixed well. Serve warm or at room temperature.

PER SERVING (*about 1 cup*): 194 Cal, 4 g Total Fat, 0 g Sat Fat, 0 g Trans Fat, 0 mg Chol, 413 mg Sod, 35 g Carb, 5 g Sugar, 8 g Fib, 5 g Prot, 40 mg Calc.

for your info

Barley is a grain that dates back thousands of years. Hulled barley, also called whole grain barley, has had its outer husk removed and is the most nutritious type of barley, but it takes the longest to cook. Scotch barley has been husked and coarsely ground, while barley grits has been hulled and cracked into small pieces. Pearl barley, the most popular type of barley, has had the husk (bran) layer removed and has also been steamed and polished.

southern-style black-eyed peas with quinoa and ham

SERVES 6

- ▲ **1 cup quinoa**
- **2 cups water**
- ▲ **1 (15½-ounce) can black-eyed peas, rinsed and drained**
- ▲ **¼ pound piece lean cooked ham, diced**
- ▲ **1 green bell pepper, chopped**
- ▲ **4 scallions, chopped**
- ▲ **1 cup diced celery**
- **½ cup chopped fresh parsley**
- ▲ **1 jalapeño pepper, seeded and minced**
- **¼ cup lemon juice**
- **1 tablespoon extra-virgin olive oil**
- **1 tablespoon sorghum or honey**

1 Put quinoa in fine sieve and hold under cool running water; drain. Combine quinoa and water in medium saucepan; bring to boil. Reduce heat and simmer, covered, until liquid is absorbed and quinoa is tender, about 10 minutes. Transfer quinoa to serving bowl; let cool slightly.

2 Add black-eyed peas, ham, bell pepper, scallions, celery, parsley, and jalapeño to quinoa; toss until mixed well.

3 To make dressing, whisk together lemon juice, oil, and sorghum in small bowl. Pour dressing over quinoa mixture and toss until coated evenly.

PER SERVING (*generous 1 cup*): 233 Cal, 6 g Total Fat, 1 g Sat Fat, 0 g Trans Fat, 18 mg Chol, 366 mg Sod, 34 g Carb, 4 g Sugar, 6 g Fib, 14 g Prot, 68 mg Calc.

now try this

Sorghum, also known as sorghum molasses and sorghum syrup, is a favorite sweetener in the South. It is made from the sweet juice that is extracted from sorghum stalks and boiled down to a thick syrup. Sorghum is used as both a table sweetener for breakfast foods and in baked goods. It is available in some supermarkets and by mail order.

pan-fried butter beans with lemon and fresh sage

SERVES 6

PER SERVING

2 teaspoons olive oil

▲ 2 (15½-ounce) cans butter beans, rinsed, drained, and patted dry

▲ 1 pint grape tomatoes

2 large garlic cloves, thinly sliced

¼ teaspoon red pepper flakes

Finely grated zest of 1 lemon

2 teaspoons lemon juice

2 teaspoons coarsely chopped fresh sage + sprigs for garnish

1 Heat oil in large nonstick skillet over medium heat. Add beans and cook, stirring once or twice, until beans are lightly browned, about 10 minutes.

2 Add tomatoes, garlic, and pepper flakes to skillet. Cook, stirring occasionally, until tomatoes are slightly softened, about 4 minutes. Remove skillet from heat. Stir in lemon zest and juice and chopped sage. Transfer bean mixture to serving bowl and garnish with sage sprigs.

PER SERVING (*about 1 cup*): 108 Cal, 2 g Fat, 0 g Sat Fat, 0 g Trans Fat, 0 mg Chol, 523 mg Sod, 24 g Carb, 3 g Sugar, 7 g Fib, 8 g Prot, 58 mg Calc.

**SMOKY BLACK BEAN CAKES
WITH GREEN SALSA CREMA**

smoky black bean cakes with green salsa crema

SERVES 4

5 PointsPlus value

PER SERVING

- ▲ 1 (15½-ounce) can no-salt-added black beans, rinsed and drained
- ▲ 3 tablespoons plain fat-free Greek yogurt
- ▲ ¾ cup medium or hot fat-free salsa
- ▲ 2 scallions, finely chopped
- ¼ cup chopped fresh cilantro
- ¼ cup plain dried whole wheat bread crumbs
- 1 tablespoon ground flaxseeds
- 1 teaspoon chipotle chili powder
- ▲ 4 cups lightly packed mesclun
- 4 (½-ounce) slices low-sodium Swiss cheese
- ▲ 1 tomato, cut into 4 slices

1 With potato masher, coarsely mash beans with 2 tablespoons of yogurt in large bowl until mixed well. Add ¼ cup of salsa, the scallions, 3 tablespoons of cilantro, 2 tablespoons of bread crumbs, the flaxseeds, and chili powder; stir until mixed well. With damp hands, shape into 4 (½-inch-thick) patties. Sprinkle patties on both sides with remaining 2 tablespoons bread crumbs and place on plate. Cover and refrigerate until firm, at least 15 minutes or up to several hours.

2 Meanwhile, to make crema, combine remaining ½ cup salsa, 1 tablespoon yogurt, and 1 tablespoon cilantro in small bowl. Cover and refrigerate.

3 Spray large nonstick skillet with nonstick spray and set over medium heat. Add patties and spray with nonstick spray. Cook until bottoms are browned and crisp, about 3 minutes. Carefully turn patties. Cook until bean cakes are heated through, 3–4 minutes longer.

4 Divide mesclun among 4 plates. Top each salad with 1 bean cake, 1 slice Swiss cheese, and 1 tomato slice. Serve with crema.

PER SERVING (*1 cup mesclun and 1 garnished bean cake*): 216 Cal, 5 g Fat, 3 g Sat Fat, 0 g Trans Fat, 10 mg Chol, 439 mg Sod, 29 g Carb, 5 g Sugar, 8 g Fib, 13 g Prot, 223 mg Calc.

for your info

Mesclun, mixed baby salad greens, is a pretty and flavorful mix of various salad greens. Most mesclun mixes include frisée, baby arugula, mizuna, oak leaf lettuce, radicchio, and mâche. When purchasing, be sure to choose an authentic mesclun mix that contains mostly whole baby lettuces, not bite-size pieces of mature greens.

grilled asparagus with couscous and a handful of herbs

SERVES 4

PointsPlus® value

PER SERVING

- ▲ **1 cup whole wheat couscous**
- ▲ **12 asparagus spears, trimmed**
- ▲ **1 cup roasted red pepper (not packed in oil), cut into ½-inch pieces**
- ▲ **4 large scallions, thinly sliced**
- **¼ cup coarsely chopped fresh parsley**
- **¼ cup lightly packed fresh basil leaves, torn**
- **¼ cup lightly packed fresh mint leaves, torn**
- **¼ cup lightly packed fresh cilantro leaves, coarsely chopped**
- ▲ **½–1 jalapeño pepper, seeded and minced**
- **Finely grated zest and juice of 1 large lemon**
- **1 tablespoon extra-virgin olive oil**
- **¼ teaspoon salt**
- **¼ teaspoon black pepper**

1 Prepare couscous according to package directions, omitting salt if desired. Let cool.

2 Meanwhile, set grill pan over medium-high heat.

3 Spray asparagus with olive oil nonstick spray. Place in grill pan in single layer. Cook, turning occasionally, until asparagus are lightly charred and just tender, about 6 minutes. Transfer to cutting board and cut into 2-inch lengths.

4 Combine couscous, asparagus, and all remaining ingredients in serving bowl; toss until mixed well. Serve at room temperature.

PER SERVING (*about 1½ cups*): 179 Cal, 4 g Total Fat, 1 g Sat Fat, 0 g Trans Fat, 0 mg Chol, 360 mg Sod, 31 g Carb, 4 g Sugar, 6 g Fib, 7 g Prot, 59 mg Calc.

stay on track

Go meatless and keep on plan with this brightly flavored vegetable dish. Make it even more tempting by sprinkling it with 4 ounces of crumbled fat-free feta cheese. This will increase the per-serving *PointsPlus* value by *1.*

bulgur with grilled balsamic-glazed summer vegetables

SERVES 4

PER SERVING

- ▲ 1¼ cups bulgur
- ▲ 2 large sweet onions, cut into ½-inch rounds
- ▲ 2 yellow squash, sliced on diagonal
- ▲ 2 red bell peppers, cut into 2-inch pieces
- ▲ 1 (1-pound) eggplant, unpeeled, quartered lengthwise and cut into ½-inch slices
- ½ teaspoon salt
- ½ teaspoon black pepper
- 2 tablespoons walnuts, finely chopped
- 2–3 tablespoons chopped fresh oregano
- 2–3 tablespoons chopped fresh mint
- 3 tablespoons balsamic vinegar glaze or to taste

1 Cook bulgur according to package directions, omitting salt if desired. Set aside.

2 Spray grill rack with nonstick spray. Preheat grill to medium or prepare medium fire.

3 Spread onions, squash, bell peppers, and eggplant on rimmed baking sheet. Spray with nonstick spray and sprinkle with salt and black pepper; toss to coat evenly.

4 Place vegetables, in batches if necessary, on grill rack or vegetable grill topper and grill, turning occasionally, until tender and charred, about 8 minutes, transferring vegetables to large bowl as they are done. Add walnuts, oregano, and mint; toss until mixed well.

5 Divide bulgur among 4 plates and top evenly with vegetable mixture; drizzle with balsamic glaze.

PER SERVING (*scant 1 cup bulgur and about 1⅓ cups vegetable mixture*): 281 Cal, 4 g Total Fat, 1 g Sat Fat, 0 g Trans Fat, 0 mg Chol, 311 mg Sod, 57 g Carb, 13 g Sugar, 16 g Fib, 10 g Prot, 95 mg Calc.

curried quinoa with cranberries, pistachios, and mint

SERVES 6

6
PointsPlus
value

PER SERVING

▲ **1 cup quinoa**

▲ **2 cups reduced-sodium vegetable broth**

1 tablespoon curry powder

½ teaspoon ground cinnamon

½ teaspoon salt

▲ **½ pound green beans, trimmed and halved**

2 teaspoons olive oil

▲ **2 celery stalks, sliced**

▲ **1 red onion, chopped**

½ cup dried cranberries

¼ cup unsalted pistachios, chopped

¼ cup lightly packed fresh mint leaves, torn if large

1 small bunch fresh chives, snipped

Finely grated zest and juice of 1 large lemon

1 Put quinoa in fine sieve and hold under cool running water; drain. Combine quinoa, broth, curry powder, cinnamon, and salt in medium saucepan; bring to boil. Reduce heat and simmer, covered, until liquid is absorbed and quinoa is tender, about 10 minutes; remove saucepan from heat and set aside.

2. Meanwhile, bring 1 inch of water to boil in medium nonstick skillet. Add green beans and cook, covered, until tender, 5–7 minutes. Drain in colander; hold under cold running water to stop cooking. Drain again. Transfer to serving bowl. Wipe skillet dry.

3. Heat oil in skillet over medium heat. Add celery and onion; cook until onion is softened, about 5 minutes. Add to green beans along with quinoa and all remaining ingredients; toss until mixed well.

PER SERVING (*scant 1 cup*): 212 Cal, 6 g Total Fat, 1 g Sat Fat, 0 g Trans Fat, 0 mg Chol, 363 mg Sod, 36 g Carb, 9 g Sugar, 6 g Fib, 6 g Prot, 65 mg Calc.

for your info

The ancient Incas referred to quinoa as the "mother grain." It is considered a complete protein because it contains all the essential amino acids. Tiny and bead shaped, quinoa should be rinsed under lukewarm water before it is cooked to remove its bitter covering.

CURRIED QUINOA WITH CRANBERRIES, PISTACHIOS, AND MINT

ancho chile red beans and rice

SERVES 4

- ▲ ½ cup brown rice
- ▲ 1 dried ancho chile pepper, seeded
-    1 cup boiling water
-    2 teaspoons olive oil
- ▲ 1 onion, finely chopped
- ▲ 1 green bell pepper, finely chopped
- ▲ 1 celery stalk, finely chopped
-    2 large garlic cloves, minced
- ▲ 1 (10-ounce) can diced tomatoes with green chiles
-    ½ cup cold water
-    1 teaspoon ground cumin
-    ½ teaspoon dried oregano
-    ½ teaspoon salt
- ▲ 1 (15½-ounce) can red kidney beans, rinsed and drained
-    ½ cup lightly packed fresh cilantro leaves
-    Hot pepper sauce

1 Prepare rice according to package directions, omitting salt if desired.

2 Meanwhile, heat small heavy skillet over medium-high heat. Add ancho pepper and cook, until toasted, about 30 seconds per side. Transfer to small bowl and pour boiling water over; let stand until hydrated, about 15 minutes. Drain and coarsely chop.

3 Heat oil in large nonstick skillet over medium heat. Add onion, bell pepper, celery, and garlic; cook, stirring, until vegetables are very tender, about 8 minutes.

4 Add tomatoes, cold water, cumin, oregano, and salt to skillet; bring to boil. Reduce heat and simmer, covered, stirring occasionally, until flavors are blended, about 6 minutes. Stir in rice and beans. Cook, stirring often, until heated through. Remove skillet from heat and stir in cilantro. Serve with pepper sauce.

PER SERVING (*1 cup*): 269 Cal, 2 g Fat, 0 g Sat Fat, 0 g Trans Fat, 0 mg Chol, 346 mg Sod, 53 g Carb, 7 g Sugar, 14 g Fib, 12 g Prot, 52 mg Calc.

Turn this robust dish into a complete meal while keeping the *PointsPlus* value the same. Serve with a generous green salad dressed with lime juice and finish off with a bowl of seasonal fruit for dessert.

new orleans dirty rice with chicken livers

SERVES 4

1½ teaspoons canola oil

▲ ¼ cup finely chopped onion

▲ ¼ cup finely chopped celery

▲ ¼ cup finely chopped green bell pepper

1 large garlic clove, minced

▲ ¾ cup quick-cooking brown rice

▲ 1¼ cups reduced-sodium chicken broth

½ teaspoon salt

⅛ teaspoon cayenne

1 bay leaf

½ pound chicken livers, coarsely ground or finely chopped

¼ cup chopped fresh parsley

1 Coat medium nonstick saucepan with ½ teaspoon of oil and set over medium heat. Add onion, celery, and bell pepper; cook, stirring, until vegetables are lightly browned, 6–8 minutes.

2 Stir garlic into vegetables and cook, stirring, until fragrant, about 1 minute. Stir in rice, broth, salt, cayenne, and bay leaf; bring to boil. Reduce heat and simmer, covered, until liquid is absorbed and rice is tender, 10–12 minutes. Remove saucepan from heat. Discard bay leaf.

3 Heat remaining 1 teaspoon oil in large nonstick skillet over medium heat. Add liver and cook, stirring, until browned, about 5 minutes. Stir in rice mixture and parsley; cook, stirring, until mixed well and heated through, about 2 minutes longer.

PER SERVING (⅔ *cup*): 160 Cal, 5 g Total Fat, 1 g Sat Fat, 0 g Trans Fat, 196 mg Chol, 367 mg Sod, 16 g Carb, 1 g Sugar, 1 g Fib, 13 g Prot, 33 mg Calc.

bhutanese red rice with grilled mushrooms and onion

SERVES 6

5
PointsPlus
value
PER SERVING

- ▲ **1 cup Bhutanese red rice or regular brown rice**
- ▲ **1 small yellow pepper**
- ▲ **1 small red bell pepper**
- ▲ **8 ounces cremini or white mushrooms, stems removed**
- ▲ **1 small red onion, very thinly sliced**
- **⅓ cup lightly packed fresh flat-leaf parsley leaves**
- **1½ tablespoons extra-virgin olive oil**
- **1–2 teaspoons sweet or hot smoked paprika (see tip page 129)**
- **1 teaspoon salt**
- **¼ teaspoon black pepper**

1 Cook rice according to package directions, omitting salt if desired.

2 Meanwhile, spray grill rack with nonstick spray and preheat grill to medium-high or prepare medium-high fire.

3 Place bell peppers and mushrooms on grill rack and grill, turning, until peppers are charred on all sides, about 15 minutes, and mushrooms are softened, browned, and nicely marked, 8–10 minutes. Transfer peppers to large zip-close plastic bag and seal bag; let steam 10 minutes.

4 When cool enough to handle, peel peppers and remove seeds; cut peppers into ½-inch pieces. Cut mushrooms into ¼-inch slices. Combine all ingredients in serving bowl; toss until mixed well. Serve warm or at room temperature.

PER SERVING (*about 1 cup*): 170 Cal, 5 g Total Fat, 1 g Sat Fat, 0 g Trans Fat, 0 mg Chol, 392 mg Sod, 30 g Carb, 2 g Sugar, 3 g Fib, 4 g Prot, 18 mg Calc.

now try this

Bhutanese red rice is a slightly sticky medium-grain rice that comes from Bhutan, which is located in the Himalayan mountains. It is only partially milled so its good-for-you bran layer is still intact.

spring vegetable risotto

SERVES 4

▲ 1 (32-ounce) carton reduced-sodium vegetable or chicken broth

▲ 2 cups mixed vegetables, such as fresh or thawed frozen baby peas, asparagus tips and thinly sliced spears, diced zucchini, and small broccoli florets

2 teaspoons olive oil

▲ 1 small onion, finely chopped

1 cup Arborio rice

¼ cup dry white wine

▲ ¼ cup fat-free half-and-half

¼ cup finely grated Parmesan cheese

¼ teaspoon salt

¼ teaspoon black pepper

2 tablespoons snipped fresh chives

1 Bring broth to simmer in medium saucepan. Keep at low simmer.

2 Put vegetables in large nonstick saucepan and add enough cold water to cover; bring to boil. Let boil 3 minutes. Drain in colander, then hold under cool running water. Drain again. Wipe saucepan dry.

3 Heat oil in same saucepan over medium heat. Add onion and cook, stirring, until softened, about 5 minutes. Add rice and cook, stirring, until translucent, about 3 minutes. Add wine and cook, stirring, until it is absorbed, about 2 minutes longer.

4 Add broth to rice, ½ cup at a time, stirring until broth is absorbed before adding more and cooking until rice is tender but still chewy in center, 25–30 minutes.

5 Stir vegetables, half-and-half, Parmesan, salt, and pepper into rice; cook just until vegetables are heated through and risotto is creamy. Divide risotto among 4 bowls and sprinkle with chives. Serve immediately.

PER SERVING (*1 cup*): 300 Cal, 4 g Total Fat, 1 g Sat Fat, 0 g Trans Fat, 4 mg Chol, 381 mg Sod, 54 g Carb, 7 g Sugar, 5 g Fib, 8 g Prot, 115 mg Calc.

charred tomato risotto with fresh herbs and parmesan

SERVES 6

5
PointsPlus®
value®

PER SERVING

- ▲ **1 large tomato (½ pound), cut into ½-inch slices**
- **1 teaspoon chopped fresh oregano**
- **1 teaspoon chopped fresh thyme**
- **¾ teaspoon salt**
- ▲ **1 (32-ounce) container reduced-sodium chicken broth**
- **1 tablespoon extra-virgin olive oil**
- ▲ **1 leek, cut lengthwise in half and thinly sliced (white and light green part only)**
- **1 large garlic clove, minced**
- **¼ teaspoon red pepper flakes**
- **1 cup short-grain rice, such as Arborio**
- **¼ cup dry vermouth**
- **¼ teaspoon black pepper**
- **⅓ cup finely grated Parmesan cheese**

1 Spray broiler rack with nonstick spray and preheat broiler.

2 Arrange tomato slices on prepared broiler rack in single layer. Combine oregano, thyme, and ¼ teaspoon of salt in cup. Sprinkle herb mixture over tomatoes. Lightly spray with nonstick spray. Broil 5 inches from heat until tomatoes are tender and lightly charred, about 4 minutes. Transfer tomato slices to cutting board. Let cool slightly then coarsely chop. Bring broth to simmer in saucepan. Keep at low simmer.

3 Meanwhile, heat oil in large saucepan over medium-low heat. Add leek and cook, stirring occasionally, until softened, about 6 minutes. Add garlic and pepper flakes; cook, stirring constantly, until fragrant, about 1 minute longer. Add rice to saucepan and increase heat to medium; cook, stirring, until rice is translucent, about 3 minutes. Add vermouth and cook, stirring constantly, until it is absorbed, about 2 minutes longer.

4 Add broth to rice, ½ cup at a time, stirring until broth is absorbed before adding more; stir in tomato with its juice, the remaining ½ teaspoon salt, and the black pepper with last addition of broth. Cook, stirring, until rice is tender but still chewy in center, 25–30 minutes. Stir in Parmesan. Divide risotto among 6 bowls. Serve immediately.

PER SERVING (⅔ *cup*): 203 Cal, 5 g Fat, 1 g Sat Fat, 0 g Trans Fat, 4 mg Chol, 409 mg Sod, 31 g Carb, 2 g Sugar, 2 g Fib, 8 g Prot, 70 mg Calc.

Top each serving of risotto with halved small cherry tomatoes for even more tempting tomato flavor and a welcome texture contrast.

creamy goat cheese polenta with mixed mushrooms

SERVES 4

5
PointsPlus©
value

PER SERVING

▲ 1 (⅓-ounce) package dried porcini mushrooms

1 cup boiling water

2 teaspoons oil

▲ 1 onion, chopped

3 large garlic cloves, minced

▲ 2 cups halved or quartered mixed mushrooms, such as white, cremini, oyster, and/or stemmed shiitakes

1 tablespoon chopped fresh thyme

½ teaspoon salt

¼ teaspoon black pepper

▲ ½ cup cherry tomatoes, halved or quartered if large

¼ cup dry white wine

3 cups cold water

⅔ cup quick-cooking polenta

2 ounces reduced-fat soft goat cheese, crumbled

1 Put dried porcini mushrooms in small bowl; cover with boiling water and let stand until softened, about 10 minutes. Pour mushroom liquid through sieve lined with paper towel set over small bowl. Reserve mushroom liquid and coarsely chop mushrooms.

2 Heat oil in large nonstick skillet over medium heat. Add onion and garlic; cook, stirring, until onion is softened, about 5 minutes. Stir in fresh mushrooms, 2 teaspoons of thyme, the salt, and pepper; cook, stirring, until mushrooms are tender, about 10 minutes. Add tomatoes, wine, and reserved mushroom liquid; bring to boil. Cook until liquid is reduced by half, about 5 minutes longer. Remove skillet from heat; keep warm.

3 Bring cold water to boil in medium saucepan; gradually whisk in polenta. Cook, stirring constantly with wooden spoon, until polenta is very thick, about 5 minutes. Remove saucepan from heat and stir in goat cheese until blended.

4 Immediately divide polenta among 4 bowls. Top evenly with mushroom mixture and sprinkle with remaining 1 teaspoon thyme.

PER SERVING (1 bowl): 189 Cal, 4 g Total Fat, 1 g Sat Fat, 0 g Trans Fat, 3 mg Chol, 353 mg Sod, 28 g Carb, 4 g Sugar, 3g Fib, 6 g Prot, 53 mg Calc.

**GARLICKY PASTA WITH WHITE BEANS
AND SMOKED MOZZARELLA**

garlicky pasta with white beans and smoked mozzarella

SERVES 6

PER SERVING

8 ounces mini farfalle (bow ties)

2 teaspoons olive oil

4 large garlic cloves, minced

▲ 1 bunch kale or escarole, trimmed and sliced (about 4 cups)

▲ 1 (15½-ounce) can small white beans, rinsed and drained

▲ 1 cup grape tomatoes, halved

▲ 1 cup reduced-sodium chicken broth

¼ teaspoon black pepper

2 ounces smoked mozzarella or other smoked cheese, coarsely shredded

1 Cook pasta according to package directions, omitting salt if desired. Drain and keep warm.

2 Meanwhile, heat oil in large nonstick skillet over medium heat. Add garlic and cook, stirring, until fragrant, about 1 minute. Add kale, a handful at a time, stirring until wilted, about 4 minutes.

3 Add beans, tomatoes, broth, and pepper to skillet; bring to simmer over medium-high heat. Cook until broth is slightly thickened, about 3 minutes. Stir in pasta and cook, stirring, until heated through, about 1 minute longer. Serve sprinkled with mozzarella.

PER SERVING (*scant 1 cup*): 262 Cal, 5 g Total Fat, 2 g Sat Fat, 0 g Trans Fat, 3 mg Chol, 415 mg Sod, 47 g Carb, 3 g Sugar, 3 g Fib, 17 g Prot, 179 mg Calc.

now try this

Smoked mozzarella has a subtle smoky flavor that adds interest to pastas, pizzas, and sandwiches. The best-quality smoked mozzarella gets its flavor from being smoked in a chamber, while lesser-quality cheeses get their smoky flavor by being coated with liquid smoke. Look for smoked mozzarella in cheese shops, specialty food stores, and farmers' markets. Try other smoked cheeses, including Gruyère, Colby, and Cheddar.

capellini with asparagus and heirloom tomatoes

SERVES 4

7 PointsPlus value

PER SERVING

▲ **6 ounces whole wheat capellini**

2 teaspoons extra-virgin olive oil

3 large garlic cloves, minced

¼ teaspoon red pepper flakes

▲ **12 asparagus, trimmed and cut into 2-inch lengths**

1½ cups water

▲ **3 tomatoes, preferably heirloom, coarsely chopped**

¼ cup chopped fresh basil

Finely grated zest of 1 lemon

¼ teaspoon salt

½ cup finely grated Parmesan cheese

1 Prepare pasta according to package directions, omitting salt if desired; drain and keep warm.

2 Meanwhile, heat oil in large nonstick skillet over medium heat. Add garlic and pepper flakes; cook, stirring, until garlic is fragrant, about 1 minute; transfer to cup.

3 Add asparagus and water to skillet; bring to boil. Reduce heat and simmer, covered, until asparagus are tender, about 4 minutes; drain.

4 Add pasta, tomatoes, basil, lemon zest, salt, and garlic mixture to skillet; cook over medium heat until heated through, about 3 minutes. Divide pasta mixture among 4 plates and sprinkle each serving with 2 tablespoons Parmesan.

PER SERVING (*about 1½ cups*): 264 Cal, 7 g Total Fat, 2 g Sat Fat, 0 g Trans Fat, 9 mg Chol, 315 mg Sod, 41 g Carb, 7 g Sugar, 7 g Fib, 12 g Prot, 165 mg Calc.

skillet pasta cake with sun-dried tomatoes and romano cheese

SERVES 8

6 PointsPlus® value

PER SERVING

▲ **1 pound whole wheat spaghetti**

1 tablespoon canola oil

▲ **1 onion, chopped**

2 large garlic cloves, minced

▲ **½ cup fat-free egg substitute**

½ cup finely grated pecorino-romano cheese

▲ **¼ cup sun-dried tomatoes (not packed in oil) finely chopped**

¼ cup chopped fresh basil

½ teaspoon salt

¼ teaspoon black pepper

¼ teaspoon red pepper flakes

1 Cook pasta according to package directions, omitting salt if desired. Drain.

2 Heat 1 teaspoon of oil in large nonstick skillet over medium heat. Add onion and cook, stirring, until softened, about 5 minutes. Add garlic and cook, stirring, until fragrant, about 1 minute longer.

3 Combine pasta, onion-garlic mixture, egg substitute, romano cheese, sun-dried tomatoes, basil, salt, black pepper, and pepper flakes in large bowl; toss until mixed well.

4 Heat 1 teaspoon oil in skillet over medium heat. Scrape pasta mixture into skillet and press with spatula to form flat cake. Cook, without stirring, until pasta cake is golden brown and crusty on bottom, about 12 minutes.

5 Place large round plate or small baking sheet on top of skillet and invert. Add remaining 1 teaspoon oil to skillet. Slide pasta cake back into skillet and cook until brown and crusty on second side, about 8 minutes longer. Slide pasta cake onto serving plate and cut into 8 wedges.

PER SERVING (*1 wedge*): 250 Cal, 4 g Total Fat, 2 g Sat Fat, 0 g Trans Fat, 8 mg Chol, 302 mg Sod, 44 g Carb, 3 g Sugar, 8 g Fib, 13 g Prot, 127 mg Calc.

stay on track

Serve this pasta cake with a generous bowl of cooked greens, such as spinach, Swiss chard, or escarole and get one or more of your daily servings of vegetables.

good and spicy peanut-sauced noodles

SERVES 6

5 PointsPlus value

PER SERVING

- 8 ounces whole wheat spaghetti
- ⅓ cup reduced-fat creamy peanut butter
- 6 tablespoons water
- 3 tablespoons hoisin sauce
- 1 tablespoon reduced-sodium soy sauce
- 1 tablespoon balsamic vinegar
- 1 tablespoon chili-garlic sauce or to taste
- 1 small red bell pepper, thinly sliced
- 1 small yellow bell pepper, thinly sliced
- 4 scallions, thinly sliced on diagonal

1 Cook pasta according to package directions, omitting salt if desired. Drain, then rinse under cold water. Drain again.

2 Whisk together peanut butter, water, hoisin, soy sauce, vinegar, and chili-garlic sauce in small bowl until smooth.

3 Transfer peanut sauce to serving bowl. Add pasta and toss until coated evenly. Add bell peppers and scallions; toss well.

PER SERVING (*about 1 cup*): 188 Cal, 5 g Total Fat, 1 g Sat Fat, 0 g Trans Fat, 0 mg Chol, 276 mg Sod, 32 g Carb, 6 g Sugar, 5 g Fib, 7 g Prot, 21 mg Calc.

soba noodles with vegetables and sesame

SERVES 6

▲ **8 ounces 100% buckwheat soba noodles**

▲ **2 red bell peppers, thinly sliced**

▲ **1 orange bell pepper, thinly sliced**

▲ **1 cup packaged broccoli slaw**

▲ **½ cucumber, cut into long matchsticks**

▲ **3 scallions, thinly sliced**

3 tablespoons red-wine vinegar

2 tablespoons reduced-sodium soy sauce

1 tablespoon Asian (dark) sesame oil

1 teaspoon superfine sugar

2 teaspoons toasted sesame seeds

1 Cook noodles according to package directions, omitting salt if desired; drain. Rinse and drain again. Transfer to serving bowl; add bell peppers, broccoli slaw, cucumber, and scallions.

2 To make dressing, whisk together vinegar, soy sauce, oil, and sugar in small bowl until sugar is dissolved. Pour over noodle mixture and toss until coated evenly. Sprinkle with sesame seeds.

PER SERVING (*about 1 cup*): 193 Cal, 4 g Total Fat, 0 g Sat Fat, 0 g Trans Fat, 0 mg Chol, 488 mg Sod, 36 g Carb, 4 g Sugar, 2 g Fib, 7 g Prot, 39 mg Calc.

stay on track

Love the earthy flavor of mushrooms? Add 6 thinly sliced white mushrooms to the vegetables in step 1.

chapter 7

how sweet it is

cakes, pies, and more; cookie jar favorites; puddings and frozen delights; fruit desserts

lemon, vanilla, and raspberry loaf cake

SERVES 12

PER SERVING

1 cup all-purpose flour

1 cup white whole wheat flour

1 tablespoon finely grated lemon zest (about 2 large lemons)

1 teaspoon baking powder

½ teaspoon baking soda

½ teaspoon salt

6 tablespoons unsalted butter, softened

1¼ cups sugar

1½ teaspoons vanilla extract

▲ ⅔ cup fat-free egg substitute

½ cup reduced-fat sour cream, at room temperature

▲ 1 (6-ounce) container fresh raspberries

1 Preheat oven to 350°F. Spray 4 x 8-inch loaf pan with nonstick spray.

2 Whisk together all-purpose flour, white whole wheat flour, lemon zest, baking powder, baking soda, and salt in medium bowl; set aside.

3 With electric mixer on medium speed, beat butter until creamy, about 1 minute. Add sugar and vanilla; beat until light and fluffy, about 4 minutes longer. Reduce speed to low and gradually beat in egg substitute. Alternately add flour mixture and sour cream, beginning and ending with flour mixture and beating just until blended. Gently fold in raspberries.

4 Scrape batter into prepared pan and spread evenly. Bake until toothpick inserted into center of cake comes out clean, about 1 hour 10 minutes. Let cool in pan on wire rack 10 minutes. Remove cake from pan and let cool completely on rack.

PER SERVING (¹⁄₁₂ *of cake*): 212 Cal, 8 g Total Fat, 5 g Sat Fat, 0 g Trans Fat, 19 mg Chol, 224 mg Sod, 34 g Carb, 16 g Sugar, 3 g Fib, 4 g Prot, 35 mg Calc.

stay on track

Here's an easy way to dress up each slice of cake while barely increasing the *PointsPlus* value. Top each serving with a dollop of plain fat-free Greek yogurt and a sprinkling of fresh raspberries and thinly sliced fresh mint (⅓ cup plain fat-free Greek yogurt per serving will increase the *PointsPlus* value by *1*).

simply exotic blood orange–walnut cake

SERVES 12

- ▲ **2 blood oranges (see tip page 74) or navel oranges, scrubbed**
- **1½ cups finely ground walnuts +⅓ cup coarsely chopped walnuts**
- **¼ cup whole wheat pastry flour**
- **1 teaspoon baking powder**
- **½ teaspoon salt**
- ▲ **2 large eggs**
- ▲ **1 large egg white**
- **¾ cup sugar**
- **1½ cups honey fat-free Greek yogurt**
- **Zest of ½ orange removed with vegetable peeler and cut into very thin strips**

1 Place whole oranges in large saucepan. Add enough cold water to cover; bring to boil. Reduce heat and simmer, covered, until oranges are very tender when pierced with tip of knife, 1–1½ hours; drain.

2 With slotted spoon, transfer oranges to cutting board. Let cool 10 minutes, then cut in quarters. Remove and discard any seeds. Transfer oranges, including peel, to food processor; pulse until pureed.

3 Preheat oven to 350°F. Spray 9-inch springform pan with nonstick spray.

4 Whisk together ground walnuts, flour, baking powder, and salt in small bowl. Whisk together eggs, egg white, and sugar in large bowl until thick and pale, about 30 seconds. Add walnut mixture to egg mixture, stirring just until no streaks of flour remain. Fold in pureed oranges until blended. Scrape batter into prepared pan.

5 Bake until toothpick inserted into center of cake comes out clean, about 45 minutes. Let cool completely on wire rack. Serve topped with yogurt, chopped walnuts, and orange zest.

PER SERVING (¹⁄₁₂ *of cake and 2 tablespoons yogurt*)**:** 174 Cal, 9 g Fat, 1 g Sat Fat, 0 g Trans Fat, 36 mg Chol, 74 mg Sod, 19 g Carb, 15 g Sugar, 2 g Fib, 6 g Prot, 69 mg Calc.

for your info

A food processor makes quick work of finely grinding the walnuts, but keep a close eye on them, as the nuts can quickly go from finely ground to walnut butter!

very chocolaty angel food cake

SERVES 12

1½ cups cake flour (not self-rising)

½ cup + 2 tablespoons unsweetened cocoa

½ teaspoon salt

2 ounces good-quality semisweet chocolate, finely chopped

▲ 12 large egg whites, at room temperature

1 teaspoon cream of tartar

1½ cups superfine sugar

1½ teaspoons vanilla extract

1 Place oven rack in lower third of oven and preheat to 375°F.

2 Sift flour, ½ cup of cocoa, and the salt into medium bowl. Stir in chocolate; set aside.

3 With electric mixer on medium speed, beat egg whites until frothy. Add cream of tartar and beat until soft peaks form when beaters are lifted. Add sugar, 2 tablespoons at a time, beating until stiff, glossy peaks form when beaters are lifted. Beat in vanilla.

4 Sift cocoa mixture, one-third at a time, over beaten egg whites, gently folding with rubber spatula just until cocoa is no longer visible. (Be careful not to overmix.)

5 Scrape batter into ungreased 10-inch tube pan; spread evenly. Bake until cake springs back when lightly pressed, 35–40 minutes. Invert pan onto its legs or neck of bottle and let cool completely. Run thin knife around edge of cake to loosen it from side and center tube of pan. Remove cake from pan and transfer to serving plate; dust with remaining 2 tablespoons cocoa.

PER SERVING (¹⁄₁₂ *of cake*): 174 Cal, 2 g Total Fat, 1 g Sat Fat, 0 g Trans Fat, 0 mg Chol, 153 mg Sod, 37 g Carb, 21 g Sugar, 2 g Fib, 6 g Prot, 11 mg Calc.

stay on track

Serving this super chocolaty angel food cake with a bowl of fresh strawberries is a delicious way to get some fiber and vitamin C into your diet.

easy triple berry pie

SERVES 8

2 tablespoons cornstarch

2 tablespoons water

▲ **1 pint fresh blueberries**

▲ **2 (6-ounce) containers fresh raspberries**

▲ **2 (6-ounce) containers fresh blackberries**

½ cup sugar

1 (6-ounce) prepared reduced-fat graham cracker crust

1 Whisk together cornstarch and water in large saucepan until smooth. Add half of blueberries, raspberries, and blackberries; stir in sugar. Bring to boil over medium-high heat, stirring frequently and pressing berries against side of saucepan with wooden spoon until crushed. Cook, stirring constantly, until mixture bubbles and thickens, about 1 minute.

2 Remove saucepan from heat and stir in remaining berries. Pour fruit filling into prepared crust. Refrigerate until filling is set, at least 5 hours or up to overnight.

PER SERVING (⅛ *of pie*): 213 Cal, 7 g Total Fat, 1 g Sat Fat, 2 g Trans Fat, 0 mg Chol, 89 mg Sod, 39 g Carb, 23 g Sugar, 6 g Fib, 2 g Prot, 25 mg Calc.

SO LIGHT LEMON CHEESECAKE
WITH BLUEBERRY SAUCE

so light lemon cheesecake with blueberry sauce

SERVES 16

5
PointsPlus®
value

PER SERVING

CHEESECAKE

12 low-fat graham crackers, broken up

1 cup + 2 tablespoons sugar

2 tablespoons unsalted butter, melted

▲ **1 (16-ounce) container fat-free sour cream**

1 (8-ounce) package light cream cheese (Neufchâtel)

1 (8-ounce) package fat-free cream cheese

▲ **2 large eggs**

▲ **2 large egg whites**

Finely grated zest of 1 lemon

1½ teaspoons vanilla extract

BLUEBERRY SAUCE

¼ cup sugar

1 tablespoon cornstarch

1 tablespoon water

▲ **1 pint fresh blueberries**

1 tablespoon lemon juice

1 Preheat oven to 350°F. Spray 9-inch springform pan with nonstick spray.

2 To make cheesecake, combine graham crackers and 2 tablespoons of sugar in food processor; pulse to make fine crumbs. Transfer to small bowl and stir in melted butter. Press crumb mixture onto bottom and halfway up side of pan. Bake until golden, 8–10 minutes; let cool on wire rack.

3 With electric mixer on medium speed, beat sour cream, light cream cheese, and fat-free cream cheese in large bowl until smooth. Add remaining 1 cup sugar, the eggs, egg whites, lemon zest, and vanilla; beat just until combined. Pour over crust.

4 Reduce oven temperature to 325°F. Bake until cheesecake is set along edge but still jiggles slightly in center, about 1 hour. Turn off oven and let cake sit in oven 1 hour longer. Refrigerate, uncovered, until chilled, at least 3 hours or up to overnight.

5 To make blueberry sauce, stir together sugar and cornstarch in medium saucepan. Stir in water. Add blueberries and bring to simmer over medium heat. Cook, stirring, until blueberries release their juice and sauce bubbles and thickens, about 5 minutes. Remove saucepan from heat and stir in lemon juice. Transfer sauce to medium bowl and refrigerate until cool.

PER SERVING (¹⁄₁₆ *of cheesecake and about 2 tablespoons sauce*): 162 Cal, 6 g Total Fat, 3 g Sat Fat, 0 g Trans Fat, 45 mg Chol, 220 mg Sod, 24 g Carb, 16 g Sugar, 1 g Fib, 6 g Prot, 121 mg Calc.

for your info

The reason some cakes and pies are baked just until they jiggle in the center is that these desserts continue to cook after they come out of the oven. If they are baked until firm in the center, they will be overbaked by the time they are completely cool.

key west lime tart with yogurt-mint topping

SERVES 10

7 low-fat honey graham crackers, broken up

3 tablespoons unsalted butter, melted

2 tablespoons sugar

⅓ cup water

1 envelope unflavored gelatin

1 (14-ounce) can fat-free sweetened condensed milk

▲ 1¼ cups plain fat-free yogurt, at room temperature

½ cup key lime or regular lime juice (about 20 key limes)

▲ 1 cup fat-free sour cream

1 tablespoon finely chopped fresh mint + 10 small sprigs for garnish

1 Preheat oven to 375°F.

2 Put crackers in food processor and pulse to make fine crumbs. Transfer to small bowl and stir in melted butter and 1 tablespoon of sugar until crumbs are evenly moistened. Press crumb mixture onto bottom and against side of 9-inch tart pan with removable bottom. Bake until crust is golden, 10–12 minutes. Let cool on wire rack.

3 Meanwhile, pour water into small saucepan; sprinkle gelatin over water and let stand until softened, about 3 minutes. Cook over low heat, stirring, until gelatin is dissolved. Remove saucepan from heat and let cool until slightly warm.

4 Whisk together condensed milk, yogurt, and lime juice in medium bowl. Gradually whisk in gelatin mixture. Pour lime mixture over crust. Refrigerate until set, at least 3 hours or up to overnight.

5 To make topping, stir together sour cream, chopped mint, and remaining 1 tablespoon sugar in small bowl. Cut tart into 10 wedges. Place dollop of topping on each wedge and garnish with mint sprig.

PER SERVING (¹⁄₁₀ *of tart and 1½ tablespoons topping*): 202 Cal, 4 g Total Fat, 2 g Sat Fat, 0 g Trans Fat, 17 mg Chol, 121 mg Sod, 36 g Carb, 30 g Sugar, 0 g Fib, 7 g Prot, 212 mg Calc.

apricot–sweet cherry crostata

SERVES 10

PER SERVING

---

1 refrigerated piecrust (from 15-ounce box), at room temperature

½ cup + 2 tablespoons sugar

1 tablespoon cornstarch

1 teaspoon finely grated lemon zest

▲ **1½ pounds apricots, halved, pitted, and cut into 1-inch wedges**

▲ **1 cup sweet cherries, pitted and halved if large**

1 Preheat oven to 400°F. Line large baking sheet with parchment paper.

2 On lightly floured work surface with floured rolling pin, roll crust into 13-inch round. Transfer to prepared baking sheet.

3 Whisk together ½ cup of sugar, the cornstarch, and lemon zest in large bowl. Add apricots and toss until mixed well. Gently stir in cherries. Spoon filling onto crust, leaving 2-inch border. Fold edge of dough over filling, pleating it as you go around. Lightly brush edge of dough with water; sprinkle edge of dough and fruit with remaining 2 tablespoons sugar.

4 Bake until filling is bubbly in center and crust is browned, about 35 minutes. Let cool 10 minutes on baking sheet on wire rack. Slide crostata with parchment onto rack. With spatula, separate crostata from parchment; slip out parchment and discard. Let crostata cool completely.

PER SERVING (*¹⁄₁₀ of crostata*): 176 Cal, 6 g Total Fat, 2 g Sat Fat, 0 g Trans Fat, 0 mg Chol, 94 mg Sod, 31 g Carb, 17 g Sugar, 2 g Fib, 2 g Prot, 14 mg Calc.

This casual free-form dessert is also known as a galette or rustic pie.

apple–dried fruit strip pie

SERVES 12

PER SERVING

CRUST

2 cups white whole wheat flour

1 tablespoon granulated sugar

½ teaspoon salt

¼ cup canola oil

2 tablespoons cold butter, cut into pieces

4–5 tablespoons ice water

▲ **1 large egg, lightly beaten, for egg wash**

FILLING

▲ **2 Golden Delicious apples, peeled, cored, and chopped**

1 cup dried apricots and/or pitted prunes, coarsely chopped

½ cup unsweetened apple juice

¼ cup water

¼ cup granulated sugar

TOPPING

½ cup confectioners' sugar

▲ **2½ teaspoons fat-free milk**

2 tablespoons sliced almonds

1 To make crust, combine flour, granulated sugar, and salt in food processor; pulse until blended. Add oil and butter; pulse until mixture resembles coarse crumbs. Pour 4 tablespoons of ice water through feed tube, pulsing just until dough forms. (If dough doesn't come together, add remaining 1 tablespoon water.) Shape dough into disk. Wrap in plastic wrap and refrigerate until firm, at least 30 minutes or up to 1 day.

2 To make filling, combine apples, apricots, apple juice, water, and granulated sugar in medium saucepan; bring to boil. Reduce heat and simmer, partially covered, stirring occasionally, until fruit is very soft and mixture is thickened, about 20 minutes. Remove saucepan from heat. Let cool 15 minutes.

3 Meanwhile, preheat oven to 375°F. Spray 10½ x 15½-inch jelly-roll pan with nonstick spray.

4 On lightly floured work surface with lightly floured rolling pin, roll dough into 11 x 16-inch rectangle, trimming dough, if needed. Transfer dough to prepared pan with long side facing you. Spread cooled filling over bottom half of dough, leaving ½-inch border on three sides. Carefully fold unfilled portion of dough over filling. With tines of fork, press edges of dough to seal. Brush dough with beaten egg. Cut 6 (½-inch) slits in top of dough to allow steam to escape.

5 Bake until crust is golden brown, 45–50 minutes. Let cool completely in pan on wire rack.

6 To make topping, stir together confectioners' sugar and milk in small bowl until smooth. Drizzle over pie and sprinkle with almonds. Let stand until glaze is set.

PER SERVING (¹⁄₁₂ *of pie*): 229 Cal, 8 g Total Fat, 1 g Sat Fat, 0 g Trans Fat, 23 mg Chol, 105 mg Sod, 37 g Carb, 19 g Sugar, 5 g Fib, 4 g Prot, 15 mg Calc.

APPLE–DRIED FRUIT
STRIP PIE

mini apple–sour cherry crumble pies

MAKES 8

3 PointsPlus value
PER SERVING

FILLING

2 Granny Smith apples, peeled, cored, and cut into ½-inch pieces

1 cup pitted fresh or thawed frozen sour cherries

¼ cup sugar

1 tablespoon minced peeled fresh ginger

1 teaspoon ground cinnamon

CRUMB TOPPING

¼ cup white whole wheat flour

¼ cup old-fashioned (rolled) oats

1 tablespoon sugar

1 tablespoon canola oil

1 Preheat oven to 375°F. Spray 8 (4-ounce) Mason jars with nonstick spray.

2 To make filling, toss together apples, cherries, sugar, ginger, and cinnamon in medium bowl. Spoon evenly into prepared jars.

3 To make topping, with fork, stir together flour, oats, sugar, and oil in small bowl until blended well. Squeeze mixture together to form loose ball, then break into small pieces. Sprinkle evenly over filling in jars. Place pies on small rimmed baking sheet. Bake until topping is golden and filling is bubbly, 35–40 minutes. Serve warm or at room temperature.

PER SERVING (*1 pie*): 93 Cal, 2 g Total Fat, 0 g Sat Fat, 0 g Trans Fat, 0 mg Chol, 1 mg Sod, 19 g Carb, 12 g Sugar, 2 g Fib, 1 g Prot, 9 mg Calc.

good morning orange-flaxseed muffins

MAKES 24

PER SERVING

1¾ cups white whole wheat flour

1 cup sugar

¼ cup ground flaxseeds

2 teaspoons baking powder

½ teaspoon salt

▲ ¾ cup fat-free milk

¼ cup canola oil

▲ 1 large egg

▲ 1 large egg white

1 tablespoon finely grated orange zest

¼ cup orange juice

1–3 teaspoons orange flower water (optional)

1 Preheat oven to 400°F. Spray 24-cup mini-muffin pan with nonstick spray.

2 Whisk together flour, ¾ cup of sugar, the flaxseeds, baking powder, and salt in large bowl. Whisk together milk, oil, egg, egg white, and orange zest in small bowl. Add milk mixture to flour mixture, stirring just until flour mixture is moistened.

3 Spoon batter into muffin cups, dividing evenly. Bake until top of muffin springs back when lightly pressed, 10–15 minutes. Let cool in pan on wire rack.

4 Meanwhile, combine remaining ¼ cup sugar and the orange juice in small microwavable bowl. Microwave on High until bubbly, about 1 minute; stir until sugar is dissolved. Stir in orange flower water, if using. With wooden skewer, poke a few holes in each muffin. Gradually brush orange-juice mixture over muffins, allowing it to seep in before brushing with more. Serve muffins warm or at room temperature.

PER SERVING (1 muffin): 91 Cal, 3 g Total Fat, 0 g Sat Fat, 0 g Trans Fat, 9 mg Chol, 103 mg Sod, 14 g Carb, 6 g Sugar, 1 g Fib, 2 g Prot, 19 mg Calc.

Start your day with ½ grapefruit, one of these grain-packed orange-scented muffins, ½ cup fat-free ricotta cheese, and 1 poached large egg, and stay satisfied for hours. This will increase the *PointsPlus* value by *5*.

pumpkin, cranberry, and thyme muffins in parchment

MAKES 12

1½ cups white whole wheat flour

1 teaspoon ground cinnamon

½ teaspoon baking soda

¼ teaspoon ground allspice

¼ teaspoon salt

1½ cups packed dark brown sugar

▲ 1 cup canned pumpkin puree (not pie mix)

▲ ½ cup fat-free milk

¼ cup canola oil

▲ 1 large egg

1 tablespoon chopped fresh thyme

▲ ½ cup coarsely chopped fresh or frozen cranberries

1 Preheat oven to 375°F. Spray 12-cup muffin pan with nonstick spray. Cut out 12 (6-inch) parchment paper squares. Center 1 parchment square over a muffin cup. Gently push it down into cup, pressing it against side and bottom and creasing parchment to fit, as needed. (Parchment will be above rim of muffin cup.) Repeat with remaining parchment squares.

2 Whisk together flour, cinnamon, baking soda, allspice, and salt in large bowl. Whisk together brown sugar, pumpkin, milk, oil, egg, and thyme in medium bowl. Add pumpkin mixture to flour mixture, stirring just until flour mixture is moistened. Fold in cranberries. Spoon batter into prepared muffin cups, filling each about three-quarters full.

3 Bake until toothpick inserted into center of muffin comes out clean, 25–30 minutes. Let muffins cool in pan on wire rack 5 minutes. Remove muffins with parchment from pan and let cool on rack. Serve warm or at room temperature.

PER SERVING (1 muffin): 225 Cal, 5 g Total Fat, 1 g Sat Fat, 0 g Trans Fat, 18 mg Chol, 119 mg Sod, 42 g Carb, 28 g Sugar, 3 g Fib, 3 g Prot, 46 mg Calc.

for your info

Paper liners can be used instead of the parchment paper squares, if you like.

PUMPKIN, CRANBERRY, AND
THYME MUFFINS IN PARCHMENT

cocoa–chocolate chip brownies

SERVES 16

PER SERVING

3 tablespoons unsalted butter

½ cup unsweetened cocoa

2 teaspoons vanilla extract

1 cup sugar

▲ 1 large egg

▲ 2 large egg whites

¾ cup all-purpose flour

½ teaspoon baking powder

¼ teaspoon salt

¾ cup semisweet chocolate chips

1 Preheat oven to 350°F. Line 8-inch square baking pan with foil, allowing foil to extend over rim of pan by 2 inches. Spray with nonstick spray.

2 Melt butter in medium saucepan over low heat. Remove saucepan from heat. Stir in cocoa and vanilla until blended; let stand until cool, about 5 minutes.

3 Whisk sugar, egg, and egg whites into cooled cocoa mixture until blended. Whisk together flour, baking powder, and salt in small bowl. Stir flour mixture into cocoa mixture until blended. Stir in chocolate chips.

4 Scrape batter into prepared pan and spread evenly. Bake until toothpick inserted into center of brownies comes out with moist crumbs clinging, 20–25 minutes. Let cool completely in pan on wire rack. Lift brownies from pan using foil as handles; cut into 16 squares.

PER SERVING (1 *brownie*): 137 Cal, 6 g Total Fat, 4 g Sat Fat, 0 g Trans Fat, 19 mg Chol, 65 mg Sod, 22 g Carb, 15 g Sugar, 2 g Fib, 3 g Prot, 10 mg Calc.

An 8-ounce glass of ice-cold fat-free milk is the perfect accompaniment for one of these brownies. This will increase the *PointsPlus* value by *2*.

coconut-vanilla macaroons

MAKES 32

1 (7-ounce) package shredded sweetened coconut

½ cup fat-free sweetened condensed milk

2 tablespoons all-purpose flour

1 teaspoon vanilla extract

½ teaspoon coconut extract

▲ 2 large egg whites

Pinch salt

1 Preheat oven to 325°F. Spray large baking sheet with nonstick spray.

2 Stir together coconut, condensed milk, flour, vanilla, and coconut extract in medium bowl until mixed well.

3 With electric mixer on high speed, beat egg whites and salt in large bowl until stiff peaks form when beaters are lifted, 3–4 minutes. With rubber spatula, gently fold one-third of beaten whites into coconut mixture just until blended. Repeat with remaining whites.

4 Drop batter by rounded teaspoonfuls, 1 inch apart, onto prepared baking sheet, making total of 32 cookies. Bake until macaroons are light golden, 20–22 minutes. Let cool on baking sheet on wire rack until cookies are firm enough to remove from baking sheet, about 20 minutes. With spatula, transfer cookies to wire racks and let cool completely.

PER SERVING (*1 cookie*): 67 Cal, 5 g Total Fat, 4 g Sat Fat, 0 g Trans Fat, 1 mg Chol, 15 mg Sod, 5 g Carb, 4 g Sugar, 1 g Fib, 1 g Prot, 13 mg Calc.

dried strawberry–granola cookies

MAKES 36

½ cup white whole wheat flour

½ cup toasted wheat germ

1 teaspoon baking powder

½ teaspoon salt

1½ cups old-fashioned (rolled) oats

½ cup low-fat granola

½ cup dried strawberries, chopped, or dried cranberries

2 tablespoons chopped unsalted pistachios

½ cup (1 stick) unsalted butter, softened

½ cup packed light brown sugar

¼ cup water

▲ 1 large egg

1 teaspoon vanilla extract

1 Place oven racks in upper and lower thirds of oven and preheat to 375°F. Spray two large baking sheets with nonstick spray.

2 Whisk together flour, wheat germ, baking powder, and salt in large bowl. Add oats, granola, dried strawberries, and pistachios; stir until combined well.

3 With electric mixer on medium speed, beat butter and brown sugar in large bowl until light and fluffy. Beat in water, egg, and vanilla just until blended. Stir in flour mixture until combined well.

4 Drop dough by level tablespoonfuls, about 1 inch apart, onto prepared baking sheets, making total of 36 cookies. With your fingers, flatten each mound to form 1½-inch cookie. Bake until cookies are golden brown and edges are deep brown, 10–12 minutes.

5 Let cookies cool slightly on baking sheets on wire racks. With spatula, transfer cookies to racks and let cool completely. Repeat with any remaining dough.

PER SERVING (*1 cookie*): 74 Cal, 3 g Total Fat, 2 g Sat Fat, 0 g Trans Fat, 13 mg Chol, 54 mg Sod, 10 g Carb, 4 g Sugar, 1 g Fib, 2 g Prot, 9 mg Calc.

now try this

Dried strawberries, available online and in specialty food stores, have an intense strawberry flavor, which makes these cookies special.

fallen dutch cocoa cookies

MAKES 42

PER SERVING

¼ cup old-fashioned (rolled) oats

1 cup white whole wheat flour

½ cup unsweetened Dutch-process cocoa

¼ teaspoon baking soda

¼ teaspoon salt

4 tablespoons unsalted butter, softened

1 cup sugar

▲ 1 large egg white

1 teaspoon vanilla extract

1 Put oats in blender and blend until finely ground.

2 Whisk together flour, cocoa, baking soda, and salt in small bowl; stir in ground oats.

3 With electric mixer on medium speed, beat butter and sugar in large bowl until creamy. Beat in egg white and vanilla. Reduce mixer speed to low and beat in flour mixture just until blended. Refrigerate dough until firm, about 15 minutes.

4 Shape dough into 11-inch log and wrap tightly in plastic wrap. Refrigerate until very firm, at least 2 hours or up to 1 day.

5 Meanwhile, preheat oven to 350°F. Spray two large baking sheets with nonstick spray.

6 Cut log into scant ¼-inch slices and place 2 inches apart on prepared baking sheets. Bake until cookies puff then fall, about 10 minutes. With spatula, transfer cookies to wire racks to cool completely.

PER SERVING (*2 cookies*): 77 Cal, 3 g Total Fat, 2 g Sat Fat, 0 g Trans Fat, 6 mg Chol, 46 mg Sod, 14 g Carb, 7 g Sugar, 1 g Fib, 1 g Prot, 4 mg Calc.

dried apricot–white chocolate cookies

MAKES 12

3 PointsPlus® value

PER SERVING

½ cup white whole wheat flour

¼ cup quick-cooking oats (not instant)

½ teaspoon baking soda

⅛ teaspoon salt

⅓ cup packed light brown sugar

3 tablespoons unsalted butter, melted and cooled

▲ 1 large egg

1 teaspoon vanilla extract

2 ounces white chocolate, cut into ¼-inch pieces

⅓ cup chopped dried apricots

1 Preheat oven to 350°F. Spray large baking sheet with nonstick spray.

2 Whisk together flour, oats, baking soda, and salt in small bowl. With electric mixer on low speed, beat brown sugar, butter, egg, and vanilla in medium bowl until blended. Add flour mixture, beating just until combined. Stir in white chocolate and apricots.

3 Drop dough by level tablespoonfuls, about 2 inches apart, onto prepared baking sheet, making total of 12 cookies. With bottom of glass dipped in flour, press each mound to form 2-inch cookie.

4 Bake until cookies are lightly browned along edges, 9–11 minutes. Let cool on baking sheet on wire rack 1 minute. With spatula, transfer cookies to wire rack to cool completely. Store in airtight container up to 2 days.

PER SERVING (*1 cookie*): 116 Cal, 5 g Total Fat, 3 g Sat Fat, 0 g Trans Fat, 27 mg Chol, 89 mg Sod, 16 g Carb, 11 g Sugar, 1 g Fib, 2 g Prot, 19 mg Calc.

for your info

To prevent the dried apricots from sticking to the knife, spray the knife with nonstick spray.

CLOCKWISE FROM TOP:
DRIED STRAWBERRY–GRANOLA COOKIES p.260,
DRIED APRICOT–WHITE CHOCOLATE COOKIES, AND
FALLEN DUTCH COCOA COOKIES p.261

chai-spiced cherry biscotti

MAKES 42

2
PointsPlus®
value
PER SERVING

2 cups white whole wheat flour

2 teaspoons baking powder

1 teaspoon anise seeds, crushed

¾ teaspoon ground cinnamon

½ teaspoon ground cardamom

¼ teaspoon ground cloves

¼ teaspoon salt

½ cup unsalted pistachios, chopped

½ cup dried sweet cherries, coarsely chopped

1 cup sugar

▲ **2 large eggs**

1 teaspoon vanilla extract

1 Place oven racks in middle and lower third of oven and preheat to 350°F. Spray large baking sheet with nonstick spray.

2 Whisk together flour, baking powder, anise seeds, cinnamon, cardamom, cloves, and salt in large bowl. Stir in pistachios and cherries. Whisk together sugar, eggs, and vanilla in medium bowl until light and pale, about 30 seconds. Add sugar mixture to flour mixture, stirring just until blended.

3 With lightly floured hands, shape dough into ball and transfer to lightly floured work surface. Divide dough in half. Shape each piece of dough into 12-inch log. Transfer logs to prepared baking sheet, spacing evenly. With damp fingers, press each log until about ½ inch high and 2 inches wide.

4 Bake logs on lower rack of oven until firm to touch, 30–35 minutes. Transfer to cutting board; let cool 10 minutes. With serrated knife, cut logs into ½-inch slices, making total of 42 biscotti. Place, cut side down, on two large baking sheets.

5 Reduce oven temperature to 300°F. Bake biscotti 10 minutes, then turn over and bake until very dry to touch and slightly crisp, about 10 minutes longer. Transfer biscotti to wire rack and let cool completely.

PER SERVING (*2 biscotti*): 94 Cal, 2 g Fat, 0 g Sat Fat, 0 g Trans Fat, 20 mg Chol, 86 mg Sod, 17 g Carb, 7 g Sugar, 2 g Fib, 3 g Prot, 16 mg Calc.

raspberry-orange tiramisu

SERVES 12

½ cup boiling water

1 tablespoon + 1 teaspoon espresso powder

1 tablespoon granulated sugar

3 tablespoons coffee liqueur, such as Kahlua

▲ 1 cup plain fat-free Greek yogurt

½ cup + 2 teaspoons confectioners' sugar

1 tablespoon finely grated orange zest

1 cup thawed frozen fat-free whipped topping

2 (3-ounce) packages ladyfingers (about 48 total)

▲ 2 (6-ounce) containers fresh raspberries

1 Combine boiling water, espresso powder, and granulated sugar in medium bowl; stir until espresso powder and sugar are dissolved. Stir in liqueur; let cool slightly.

2 Stir together yogurt, ½ cup of confectioners' sugar, and the orange zest in large bowl. Gently fold in whipped topping until blended.

3 Line bottom of 3-quart baking dish or casserole with half of ladyfingers, arranging them cut side up. Brush with half of espresso mixture and top with half of yogurt mixture. Repeat with remaining ladyfingers, espresso mixture, and yogurt mixture. Cover dish with plastic wrap, being careful not to let plastic touch tiramisu; refrigerate until chilled, at least 4 hours or up to 2 days.

4 Just before serving, scatter raspberries over tiramisu and dust with remaining 2 teaspoons confectioners' sugar. Cut into 12 squares.

PER SERVING (*1 square*): 126 Cal, 2 g Total Fat, 0 g Sat Fat, 0 g Trans Fat, 31 mg Chol, 32 mg Sod, 23 g Carb, 11 g Sugar, 2 g Fib, 4 g Prot, 28 mg Calc.

for your info

The combination of raspberries and orange is classic and delicious, but you can use other berries, such as blueberries or blackberries, if you like.

cherry-almond clafouti

SERVES 8

PER SERVING

- ▲ **1 pound sweet cherries, pitted**
- **1½ tablespoons Kirsch (cherry brandy)**
- **1 cup low-fat (1%) milk**
- ▲ **1 cup fat-free egg substitute**
- **⅔ cup all-purpose flour**
- **¼ cup + 2 tablespoons granulated sugar**
- **1 teaspoon vanilla extract**
- **Pinch salt**
- ▲ **1 cup fat-free half-and-half**
- **⅓ cup sliced almonds**
- **1 tablespoon confectioners' sugar**

1 Preheat oven to 375°F. Spray 10-inch pie plate, quiche dish, or 2-quart shallow round baking dish with nonstick spray.

2 Toss together cherries and Kirsch in large bowl; set aside.

3 Pour milk into medium microwavable bowl. Microwave on High until hot, about 2 minutes.

4 Pour egg substitute into medium bowl. Gradually whisk in flour until smooth. Whisk in ¼ cup of granulated sugar, the vanilla, and salt, then whisk in half-and-half and hot milk. Pour liquid from soaked cherries into batter and mix well. Spread cherries evenly in prepared dish; pour batter over.

5 Bake clafouti 15 minutes. Sprinkle almonds over clafouti and sprinkle with remaining 2 tablespoons granulated sugar. Bake until clafouti is puffed and golden and knife inserted into center comes out clean, about 20 minutes longer. Let cool on wire rack until warm, about 20 minutes. Dust with confectioners' sugar and cut into 8 wedges.

PER SERVING (*1 wedge*): 174 Cal, 2 g Total Fat, 0 g Sat Fat, 0 g Trans Fat, 2 mg Chol, 102 mg Sod, 31 g Carb, 20 g Sugar, 2 g Fib, 7 g Prot, 105 mg Calc.

for your info

Kirsch, also known as *Kirschwasser* (cherry water), is clear cherry brandy distilled from cherry juice and pits. Kirsch's claim to fame is cherries jubilee, a dessert in which cherries and Kirsch are flamed and served over vanilla ice cream.

pumpkin bread pudding with golden raisins

SERVES 12

PER SERVING

- ▲ **3 cups fat-free half-and-half**
- ▲ **1 cup fat-free egg substitute**
- **½ cup packed light brown sugar**
- **1 teaspoon ground cinnamon**
- **¼ teaspoon ground nutmeg**
- **¼ teaspoon salt**
- **⅛ teaspoon ground cloves**
- ▲ **1 cup canned pumpkin puree (not pie mix)**
- **2 teaspoons vanilla extract**
- **1 (1-pound) loaf day-old challah or other egg bread, cut into 1-inch pieces**
- **½ cup golden raisins or dried currants**
- **½ cup walnuts, chopped**

1 Bring half-and-half to boil in medium saucepan over medium-high heat; remove saucepan from heat.

2 Whisk together egg substitute, brown sugar, cinnamon, nutmeg, salt, and cloves in medium bowl. Slowly whisk ½ cup of hot half-and-half into brown sugar mixture.

3 Whisk half-and-half mixture back into saucepan and set over medium-low heat. Cook, whisking constantly, until custard thickens and coats back of spoon, about 5 minutes. Immediately pour custard through sieve set over medium bowl. Whisk in pumpkin and vanilla. Add bread and raisins to bowl, gently stirring until moistened. Let stand about 20 minutes. Stir in walnuts.

4 Meanwhile, preheat oven to 325°F. Spray 10-cup baking dish or casserole with nonstick spray.

5 Pour pudding mixture into prepared baking dish. Cover baking dish tightly with foil and place in roasting pan. Add enough boiling water to roasting pan to come halfway up sides of baking dish. Bake 1 hour. Uncover and bake until knife inserted into center comes out clean, about 15 minutes longer. Serve warm or at room temperature.

PER SERVING (*¹⁄₁₂ of bread pudding*): 218 Cal, 6 g Total Fat, 2 g Sat Fat, 0 g Trans Fat, 28 mg Chol, 176 mg Sod, 38 g Carb, 19 g Sugar, 3 g Fib, 6 g Prot, 43 mg Calc.

oh-so-silky double chocolate–hazelnut pudding

SERVES 6

¼ cup sugar

2 tablespoons cornstarch

▲ 2 cups fat-free half-and-half

2 ounces good-quality semisweet chocolate, finely chopped

1 ounce good-quality bittersweet chocolate, finely chopped

▲ 1 large egg yolk

1 tablespoon hazelnut liqueur, such as Frangelico

1 teaspoon vanilla extract

Pinch salt

1 Whisk together sugar and cornstarch in medium saucepan. Slowly whisk in half-and-half until smooth. Set saucepan over medium heat; cook, whisking constantly, until mixture bubbles and thickens, 6–8 minutes. Remove saucepan from heat. Stir in semisweet and bittersweet chocolates, stirring until chocolate is melted and smooth.

2 Whisk together egg yolk, liqueur, vanilla, and salt in medium bowl. Slowly whisk half of hot half-and-half mixture into yolk mixture. Add yolk mixture to saucepan and cook over low heat, stirring constantly with wooden spoon, just until mixture thickens, 1–2 minutes.

3 Immediately divide pudding among 6 dessert dishes; let cool to room temperature. Refrigerate, covered, until thoroughly chilled and set, at least 3 hours or up to 2 days.

PER SERVING (1 pudding): 261 Cal, 8 g Total Fat, 4 g Sat Fat, 0 g Trans Fat, 52 mg Chol, 139 mg Sod, 39 g Carb, 29 g Sugar, 1 g Fib, 6 g Prot, 166 mg Calc.

ruby red grapefruit and mint granita

SERVES 6

PER SERVING

3 cups red grapefruit juice

1 cup boiling water

½ cup superfine sugar

2 tablespoons chopped fresh mint + 6 sprigs for garnish

▲ 2 (6-ounce) containers fresh blackberries, halved

1 Whisk together grapefruit juice, water, and sugar in large bowl until sugar is dissolved. Stir in chopped mint. Pour mixture into 9 x 13-inch baking pan. Cover tightly with foil and freeze until frozen along edges, about 1 hour. With fork, scrape ice at edges in toward center. Repeat every 30 minutes until granita is semi-firm, about 3 hours.

2 To serve, use fork to scrape across surface of granita, transferring ice shards to 6 dessert dishes or wineglasses. Spoon blackberries around granita and garnish each serving with mint sprig.

PER SERVING (¾ cup granita and ⅓ cup blackberries): 89 Cal, 0 g Total Fat, 0 g Sat Fat, 0 g Trans Fat, 0 mg Chol, 3 mg Sod, 23 g Carb, 12 g Sugar, 0 g Fib, 1 g Prot, 14 mg Calc.

for your info

There are several varieties of red grapefruit, including Ruby Red, Rio Red, and Henderson/Ray. All were discovered in Texas at the beginning of the twentieth century, are seedless, and retain some degree of red color in their peel.

ripe strawberry and lime sorbet

SERVES 8

2
PointsPlus®
value
PER SERVING

2 cups water

½ cup sugar

2 (3-inch) strips lime zest

3 tablespoons lime juice

▲ **5½ cups fresh strawberries**

1 Combine water, sugar, and lime zest in medium saucepan. Bring to boil, stirring until sugar is dissolved. Reduce heat and simmer 5 minutes. Remove saucepan from heat and let cool about 5 minutes. Discard zest and stir in lime juice.

2 Puree 1 cup of lime-sugar syrup mixture with 3½ cups of strawberries in food processor or blender. Stir strawberry mixture into remaining sugar syrup. Pour mixture through sieve set over medium bowl, pressing hard on solids to extract as much liquid as possible. Discard solids. Cover strawberry mixture and refrigerate until thoroughly chilled, at least 2 hours or up to overnight.

3 Transfer strawberry mixture to ice-cream maker and freeze according to manufacturer's instructions. Transfer sorbet to freezer container and freeze until firm, at least 2 hours or up to 6 hours.

4 To serve, slice remaining 2 cups strawberries. Scoop sorbet evenly into 8 dessert dishes and top with sliced strawberries.

PER SERVING (*about ½ cup sorbet and ¼ cup sliced strawberries*): 63 Cal, 0 g Total Fat, 0 g Sat Fat, 0 g Trans Fat, 0 mg Chol, 3 mg Sod, 17 g Carb, 14 g Sugar, 2 g Fib, 1 g Prot, 18 mg Calc.

stay on track

A serving of this refreshing sorbet is a good way to satisfy your sweet tooth while adding fiber and vitamin C to your day.

black and blue berry yogurt pops

MAKES 8

▲ **1½ cups fresh or frozen blackberries**

▲ **1 cup fresh or frozen blueberries**

▲ **1 medium ripe banana**

1 (6-ounce) container honey fat-free Greek yogurt

½ cup light (reduced-fat) coconut milk

3 tablespoons light agave nectar (see tip page 109)

Finely grated zest of 1 lime

1 tablespoon lime juice

1 teaspoon almond extract

1 Puree blackberries in food processor. Pour puree through fine-mesh sieve set over medium bowl, pressing hard on solids to extract as much liquid as possible. Discard solids.

2 Combine blueberries, banana, yogurt, coconut milk, agave nectar, lime zest and juice, and almond extract in food processor; process until smooth. Add blackberry puree and pulse until blended.

3 Divide berry mixture evenly among 8 (⅓-cup) popsicle molds. Cover and freeze until firm, about 4 hours or up to overnight.

4 To serve, dip bottom of each mold in hot water to loosen, about 10 seconds. Remove pops from molds. Serve at once.

PER SERVING (*1 ice pop*): 85 Cal, 1 g Fat, 0 g Sat Fat, 0 g Trans Fat, 0 mg Chol, 10 mg Sod, 17 g Carb, 12 g Sugar, 3 g Fib, 3 g Prot, 37 mg Calc.

STRAWBERRY-VANILLA
ICE-CREAM SANDWICHES

strawberry-vanilla ice-cream sandwiches

SERVES 15

PER SERVING

¾ cup white whole wheat flour

3 tablespoons unsweetened cocoa

½ teaspoon baking soda

¾ cup sugar

5 tablespoons light stick butter

2 tablespoons water

2 ounces unsweetened chocolate, finely chopped

▲ 1 large egg

1½ cups vanilla fat-free ice cream, slightly softened

1½ cups strawberry fat-free frozen yogurt, slightly softened

¼ cup walnuts, toasted and finely chopped

1 cup fat-free chocolate sauce or syrup

1 Preheat oven to 350°F. Spray 10½ x 15½-inch jelly-roll pan with nonstick spray. Line pan with foil; spray foil with nonstick spray and lightly dust with flour, shaking out excess.

2 Whisk together flour, cocoa, and baking soda in small bowl. Combine sugar, butter, and water in medium saucepan and bring to boil over medium heat, stirring occasionally.

3 Remove saucepan from heat and add chocolate, stirring until chocolate is melted; let cool 10 minutes. Whisk in egg, then stir in flour mixture until blended. Scrape batter into prepared pan and spread evenly. Bake until toothpick inserted into center of brownie comes out clean, about 12 minutes. Let cool in pan on wire rack, then refrigerate 10 minutes.

4 Invert brownie layer onto cutting board and carefully peel off foil. Cut brownie lengthwise in half, forming 2 (5 x 15-inch) rectangles. Spread vanilla ice cream over one rectangle and strawberry frozen yogurt over other rectangle. Sprinkle walnuts over ice cream. Sandwich layers together. Cover with plastic wrap and freeze until firm, about 3 hours.

5 Remove plastic wrap and place frozen sandwich on cutting board. With heavy knife, cut lengthwise into thirds. Slice each third into 5 small rectangular sandwiches. Wrap each sandwich in plastic wrap and place in large zip-close plastic freezer bag. Freeze up to 1 week.

6 To serve, unwrap each sandwich and place on plate. Drizzle with about 1 tablespoon chocolate syrup.

PER SERVING (*1 sandwich*): 214 Cal, 7 g Total Fat, 3 g Sat Fat, 0 g Trans Fat, 23 mg Chol, 116 mg Sod, 37 g Carb, 16 g Sugar, 3 g Fib, 4 g Prot, 66 mg Calc.

lavender and lemongrass poached pears

SERVES 8

3 cups water

1 cup dry white wine

¼ cup sugar

2 (4-inch) stalks lemongrass, tender white part only, halved lengthwise (see tip page 48)

1 (3-inch) length vanilla bean, split

1 tablespoon dried lavender buds (see tip page 119)

Pinch salt

▲ **4 large firm-ripe Bosc or Bartlett pears (about 7 ounces each)**

1 Combine water, wine, sugar, lemongrass, vanilla, lavender, and salt in large saucepan and bring to boil; boil 10 minutes. Remove saucepan from heat.

2 Meanwhile, peel pears; cut lengthwise in half and remove core. Add pears to saucepan and set over low heat. Simmer, covered, until pears are tender when pierced with fork, 10–15 minutes. With slotted spoon, transfer pears to large shallow bowl.

3 Bring poaching liquid to boil over high heat; boil until reduced to about 1 cup, about 10 minutes. Pour syrup through fine-mesh sieve set over small bowl. Pour poaching liquid over pears. Cool pears slightly and serve or refrigerate, covered, turning occasionally, until well chilled, at least 3 hours or up to 2 days.

PER SERVING (*1 pear half with 2 tablespoons poaching syrup*): 98 Cal, 0 g Fat, 0 g Sat Fat, 0 g Trans Fat, 0 mg Chol, 21 mg Sod, 21 g Carb, 13 g Sugar, 3 g Fib, 0 g Prot, 14 mg Calc.

melon with ginger-lime syrup

SERVES 4 • 20 MINUTES

3 PointsPlus® value PER SERVING

2 tablespoons sugar

½ teaspoon finely grated lime zest

1 tablespoon lime juice

1 tablespoon cold water

▲ ½ large cantaloupe, seeded, peeled, and cut into 1-inch dice

▲ 1 cup (1-inch) diced seedless watermelon

▲ 1 (6-ounce) container fresh raspberries, preferably golden

2 tablespoons finely chopped crystallized ginger

1 Stir together sugar, lime zest and juice, and water in cup. Let stand 5 minutes; stir until sugar is dissolved.

2 Divide cantaloupe, watermelon, and raspberries among 4 dessert dishes. Drizzle lime syrup evenly over each serving and sprinkle evenly with ginger.

PER SERVING (*1 dessert*): 87 Cal, 1 g Total Fat, 0 g Sat Fat, 0 g Trans Fat, 0 mg Chol, 18 mg Sod, 22 g Carb, 16 g Sugar, 4 g Fib, 2 g Prot, 24 mg Calc.

for your info

You can use almost any variety of melon and berries you like in this fruit compote.

recipes by *PointPlus* value

CHARRED SUMMER SQUASH WITH
PARMESAN AND MINT, p. 199

recipes that work with the Simply Filling technique

SOY AND HONEY–GLAZED TOFU–VEGETABLE SKEWERS, p. 167

index

dry and liquid measurement equivalents

If you are converting the recipes in this book to metric measurements, use the following chart as a guide.

TEASPOONS	TABLESPOONS	CUPS	FLUID OUNCES	VOLUME	
3 teaspoons	1 tablespoon		½ fluid ounce	¼ teaspoon	1 milliliter
6 teaspoons	2 tablespoons	⅛ cup	1 fluid ounce	½ teaspoon	2 milliliters
8 teaspoons	2 tablespoons plus	⅙ cup 2 teaspoons		1 teaspoon	5 milliliters
12 teaspoons	4 tablespoons	¼ cup	2 fluid ounces	1 tablespoon	15 milliliters
15 teaspoons	5 tablespoons	⅓ cup minus 1 teaspoon		2 tablespoons	30 milliliters
16 teaspoons	5 tablespoons plus 1 teaspoon	⅓ cup		3 tablespoons	45 milliliters
18 teaspoons	6 tablespoons	¼ cup plus 2 tablespoons	3 fluid ounces	¼ cup	60 milliliters
24 teaspoons	8 tablespoons	½ cup	4 fluid ounces	⅓ cup	80 milliliters
30 teaspoons	10 tablespoons	½ cup plus 2 tablespoons	5 fluid ounces	½ cup	120 milliliters
32 teaspoons	10 tablespoons plus 2 teaspoons	⅔ cup		⅔ cup	160 milliliters
36 teaspoons	12 tablespoons	¾ cup	6 fluid ounces	¾ cup	175 milliliters
42 teaspoons	14 tablespoons	1 cup minus 2 tablespoons	7 fluid ounces	1 cup	240 milliliters
45 teaspoons	15 tablespoons	1 cup minus 1 tablespoon		1 quart	950 milliliters
48 teaspoons	16 tablespoons	1 cup	8 fluid ounces		

LENGTH	
1 inch	25 millimeters
1 inch	2.5 centimeters

OVEN TEMPERATURE			
250˚F	120˚C	400˚F	200˚C
275˚F	140˚C	425˚F	220˚C
300˚F	150˚C	450˚F	230˚C
325˚F	160˚C	475˚F	250˚C
350˚F	180˚C	500˚F	260˚C
375˚F	190˚C	525˚F	270˚C

WEIGHT	
1 ounce	30 grams
¼ pound	120 grams
½ pound	240 grams
1 pound	480 grams

Note: Measurement of less than ⅛ teaspoon is considered a dash or a pinch.
Metric volume measurements are approximate.